Knowledge Set

Nutrition and Well-being

Carolyn Aldworth

www.heinemann.co.uk
✓ Free online support
✓ Useful weblinks
✓ 24 hour online ordering

01865 888118

D0528230

Heinemann is an imprint of Pearson Education Limited, a company incorporated in England and Wales, having its registered office at Edinburgh Gate, Harlow, Essex, CM20 2JE. Registered company number: 872828

www.heinemann.co.uk

Heinemann is the registered trademark of Pearson Education Limited

Text © Carolyn Aldworth 2008

First published 2008

12 11 10 09 08
10 9 8 7 6 5 4 3 2 1

British Library Cataloguing in Publication Data is available from the British Library on request.

ISBN 978 0 435402 38 9

Edited by Alex Gray and Jane Anson
Typeset by Saxon Graphics Limited, Derby
Original illustrations © Pearson Education Limited 2008, apart from p. 34 Makaton symbols © The Makaton Charity
Cover photo/illustration © FlowerPhotos.com/Noelle Pollington
Printed in the UK by Ashford Colour Press Ltd

Photo acknowledgements
The author and publisher would like to thank the following individuals and organisations for permission to reproduce photographs:
Page 2: © Photofusion/Karen Robinson; page 11 Science Photo Library/Garry Watson; page 13 (left): © Science Photo Library/Susumu Nishinaga; page 13 (right): Science Photo Library/Hybrid Medical Animation; page 21 (above): © Science Photo Library/Dr P. Marazzi; page 21 (below): © Stephen Hay/Photographers Direct; pages 23, 92: © 2002, Hemera™ Technologies Inc; page 30: © Alamy/Abraham Menashe; page 38 (above): © Photofusion/Paul Baldesare; page 38 (below): Pearson Education Ltd/Lord & Leverett; page 41: © Alamy/Photofusion; pages 48, 52: © Pearson Education Ltd/Jules Selmes; page 49, 50, 51, 82 © Patterson; page 65 © Pearson Education Ltd/Gareth Boden; page 73: © Stephen Hay/Photographers Direct; page 75: © Richard Smith/Pearson Education Ltd; page 92 © 2003–2008, Shutterstock Images LLC; page 97 © Pearson Education Limited/Tudor Photography.

Contents

Introduction

Knowledge sets have been created by Skills for Care. The idea behind each knowledge set is to provide key learning outcomes for specific areas of work within adult social care. This means that employers and training providers can use a knowledge set to provide in-house training as part of employees' continuing professional development. The advantage of using a knowledge set for the basis of training is that both employers and those who have undertaken training can be assured that a minimum standard has been reached. The knowledge sets also ensure consistency in knowledge and understanding across organisations and services.

This book has been written by Carolyn Aldworth, a lecturer in health and social care and former district nurse. Using this book, in conjunction with the Skills for Care knowledge set, will:

- provide essential learning for all aspects of working with people with specific nutrition and well-being needs, improving confidence and skills
- improve practice in order to meet the individual needs of those who receive care, allowing the opportunity to make a real difference
- support those completing NVQ and other training, providing evidence for portfolios
- support transition between different service settings in the social care sector
- ensure up-to-date and good practice.

The book is divided into the four main areas of the knowledge set:

- Preparation/presentation of food and drink
- Roles and boundaries
- Diet and well-being
- Legislation and guidance in relation to food and drink

These sections are further broken down into manageable topics, with spreads covering one or more learning outcomes. The following features have been designed to enhance the learning experience:

 Activities – completion of the suggested activities and tasks will develop understanding and skills.

 Care scenarios – real-life situations allowing knowledge to be put into practice.

 Look it up – pointers to recognised reference sources that allow comparison of current knowledge with accepted good practice. You may also be asked to investigate your care setting's current procedures and practices.

 Reflection – explore your level of knowledge as well as your thoughts, actions and behaviours.

Remember – key concepts and facts are highlighted and reinforced.

 Question check – test your understanding and recall of a topic.

Space has often been provided for note-taking or the completion of activities and tables, although a notebook or workbook can be used alongside this book in order to expand on certain areas.

This book not only covers the learning outcomes for those undertaking training, but also includes a section for those developing or leading training sessions. The Trainer notes provide the answers to Care scenarios, guidance on the completion of activities and also expands on the knowledge given in the four main knowledge set areas. In addition, guidance on activities within the book often includes ideas and suggestions for developing an activity and expanding on learning opportunities. Useful icons appear with each activity guidance feature, suggesting how long to spend on the activity and any materials that will be needed (e.g. pens, flipchart, OHP).

The Student Log section of this book details all four main areas of the knowledge set for nutrition and well-being, along with the learning outcomes. Space is provided for trainees to log their progress and record those learning outcomes they have covered. In addition, the tables can also be used to map the content of this book against NVQ courses and any other relevant training being undertaken.

If those completing training are working with younger people with dementia, alcohol-related dementias or learning disabilities, it is recommended that this book is used in conjunction with specific guidance on the issues that affect these groups.

Used either as part of a training package or own its own by an individual, this *Knowledge set for nutrition and well-being* will prove to be an invaluable resource for those developing their career in the adult social care sector.

Acknowledgements

Pearson would like to thank Skills for Care for giving permission to reproduce the tables of learning outcomes used in the Student Log section of this book (see pages 136–41).

The publisher and author would like to thank Professor Susan Holmes, of Canterbury Christ Church University, for her constructive review of this book.

The author would also like to thank Colin, Charlotte and Jonathan Aldworth, and Pen Gresford at Heinemann, for their support during the writing of this book.

The author and publisher would like to thank the following individuals and organisations for permission to reproduce text: pages 4, 7, 8, 96, 102: © Crown copyright material is reproduced with the permission of the Controller of HMSO and Queen's Printer for Scotland; page 31: Mental Health Foundation; page 55: Age Concern; page 56 material from 'Malnutrition Within an Ageing Population: A Call for Action' report (2005), European Nutrition for Health Alliance; page 87 adapted extract from Royal College of Nursing website www. rcn.org.uk.

Every effort has been made to contact copyright holders of material reproduced in this book. Any omissions will be rectified in subsequent printings if notice is given to the publishers.

Preparation and presentation of food and drink

1.1 Understand the common factors that affect dietary requirements

Florence Robinson is 93 years of age. She has been admitted to hospital following a fall. Her daughter, Anne, has come with her and looks very worried about her mother. She tells you that her mother has been a very active woman, and only last year she went on holiday to Scotland. In the last six months she seems to have aged about ten years. She has lost her appetite and her weight has dropped by a stone and a half.

Florence looks pale, and her teeth don't fit. She is very withdrawn and she refuses the cup of tea you offer her when she arrives on the ward. You ask her questions, but she doesn't answer and seems vague.

This is not an uncommon situation. There are many reasons why people suddenly lose interest in eating and drinking. Florence could be depressed, or could have a chronic illness or infection; she may have cancer, or a sore mouth, or she may be developing dementia.

When caring for people you need to be able to notice when something is wrong and know what to do, whether it is something you can do yourself, or just that you need to inform a senior member of staff.

Care settings offer a unique opportunity to ensure that their service users are well nourished, yet the National Diet and Nutrition Survey (1998) showed that 15% of men and 16% of women in care homes were **malnourished**. The situation in hospital was even worse. Of those admitted to hospital, 40% are undernourished, and according to the charity Age Concern (2006), six out of ten older people are at risk of becoming malnourished or **dehydrated** or their condition getting worse in hospital. Patients who are malnourished stay in hospital for a longer time, require more medications, and are more likely to suffer from infections. For more information on malnourishment of service users, go to www.ageconcern.org.uk.

It is rewarding to see your service users enjoying their food and drinking well, especially when they are on a special diet, for which they might have been told to avoid some of their favourite foods.

malnourished

in a state (or condition) where a person is not receiving adequate nourishment. May involve eating too little or too much of essential nutrients

dehydrated

in a state where the body's normal water content is reduced by 1% or more

Activity 1

Masoomah Ali is 78 years old. She has diabetes mellitus and has very poor sight. She lives in a sheltered housing scheme. Errol Murphy, a care worker, comes to her house daily to cook her lunch, do some shopping and do a few household chores.

Errol is proud of his use of initiative, and he makes a list and shops for Mrs Ali, buying her a wide variety of foods to ensure that she has a good nutritious diet.

He likes to surprise her with unusual meals. He has spent a lot of time on the Internet learning about diabetes to make sure that the meals he produces are suitable.

■ Do you think Errol is providing a good service to Mrs Ali?

_____

■ Is there any way Errol could improve his care practice?

_____

When you have finished your training on the Nutrition and Well-being Knowledge Set, come back to this activity to see if your answers have changed.

In this section you will learn the many different factors that can influence the food you offer service users in your care.

> You can read about what is required to make a well-balanced diet on pages 84–96. The National Minimum Standards for Care Homes for Older People (see pages 118–19) stress the importance of an enjoyable and healthy diet in contributing to the well-being of care home residents.

What you need to learn

- How age affects dietary requirements.
- How culture can influence dietary choice.
- How religion affects dietary choice.
- Medical conditions requiring special diets.
- Timing and availability of food and drink.
- Personal choice.

In order to be able to appreciate factors that affect dietary requirements, you need to have some knowledge of what those requirements are. Section 3.1 (pages 84–96) has detailed information about dietary components and the constituents of a balanced diet, and you may decide to study that section first.

Diet can be complicated, but it has been recognised over the years that most people are either unable, or not prepared, to follow complicated advice. The Food Standards Agency has created eight tips for making healthier choices. The practical tips are aimed to help people to achieve a healthy balanced diet as part of a healthier lifestyle. Use these tips for help in answering any questions in sections 1 and 2 where you need to suggest menus:

- Base your meals on starchy foods
- Eat lots of fruit and veg
- Eat more fish – including a portion of oily fish per week
- Cut down on saturated fat and sugar
- Try to eat less salt – no more than 6g a day
- Get active and try to be a healthy weight
- Drink plenty of water
- Don't skip breakfast

In addition, you need to be aware of the essential nutrients in the diet:

- Protein – from meat, fish, dairy foods or a variety of pulses and non-meat protein alternatives
- Carbohydrate – from bread, potatoes, rice, pasta
- Fats – preferably vegetable sources such as sunflower or olive oil
- Minerals – see chart on pages 93–4
- Vitamins – see chart on page 95

How age affects dietary requirements

This section helps you to understand how dietary needs change across a person's lifespan. A diet suitable for a child is not likely to be right for an older person. You need to be aware of appropriate dietary needs for people of different ages.

Infancy

When a baby is born its digestive system is still immature and is unable to digest many foods. For this reason babies' nutritional needs are entirely met by milk, preferably breast milk, which is a complete food for babies. Babies who are bottle-fed with powdered baby milk may need extra drinks of cooled boiled water in warm weather. It is essential that the powdered milk is made up according to the instructions on the container, as too little powder will mean that the baby will not put on weight and too much can damage the kidneys. Bottles must be sterilised thoroughly to ensure that the baby does not get diarrhoea and sickness, which can be very serious.

Weaning–4 years

The age at which solid foods are introduced varies, but it is recommended that weaning does not start until six months of age. Experts believe that this lessens a baby's chances of developing food allergies. Signs that a baby is ready for some solid food include shorter lengths of time between demands for food, and still showing signs of hunger after taking a full feed.

The first foods are given in tiny amounts to get the baby used to new tastes and to ensure that any foods that cause allergies can easily be identified. Healthy eating habits should be started as soon as weaning begins. Baby rice and puréed fruits and vegetables are good first foods, however strawberries should be avoided, as they are more likely to cause an allergic reaction. By 9 months the texture can be lumpier. By 12–18 months the infant should be on a normal diet, although the food will need to be cut up, and you should stay nearby in case of choking. You should avoid salty foods, such as gravy, which can damage the kidneys. It is also wise to avoid foods that are very sweet. Cows' milk can be introduced at 12 months, but should be full-fat, not skimmed or semi-skimmed, as it contains more calories. Young children cannot eat large amounts of food, so they need calorie-rich foods for energy. Young children also need foods that are high in calcium and protein, as they are growing fast. Otherwise, a varied diet should provide for all of their needs.

Childhood and adolescence (4–18 years)

Growth and development are fast during this phase, and children should be very active. Protein and carbohydrates are therefore very important. The diet should follow the Food Standards Agency guidelines outlined on page 96. If children are hungry between meals, healthy snacks such as fruit or toast should be offered. Crisps and sweets will increase the risk of obesity and tooth decay.

Adulthood (19–65 years)

Once growth has stopped, adults need to maintain their weight, but should try to avoid putting on extra weight. High-fat foods can lead to obesity and can increase the risk of heart disease. Animal fats, in particular, should be kept to a minimum, as they are high in cholesterol. Being overweight can also increase the chances of developing arthritis, diabetes, and cancer. To reduce the risk of developing high blood pressure, salt should be limited to 6g per day (about 1 teaspoonful). High-sugar foods should be a treat rather than a regular part of the diet. Alcohol consumption has been linked with several cancers including cancer of the breast. However, asking people to avoid alcohol altogether does not agree with recommendations from the British Heart Foundation, which found that moderate drinking can protect against heart disease. A good compromise is to limit alcohol consumption to 1 unit a day for women and 2 units a day for men (World Cancer Research Fund 2007).

1 unit of alcohol is:

half a pint of 3.5% proof beer, cider or lager
125ml glass of 9% proof wine
25ml measure of spirits

It is worth remembering that the size of the average wine glass has increased, with many now holding 175ml or even 250ml. In addition, much of the wine on sale is stronger than it used to be (up to 12% or 13% proof). These factors make it easy for people to consume more alcohol than they realise.

Activity 2

Do you eat a healthy diet? Look at the chart below and decide whether your diet could be improved.

	Always	Often	Sometimes	Never
Is a third of your diet made up of starchy foods?				
Do you eat five portions of fruit and vegetables per day?				
Do you eat oily fish at least once a week?				
Do you try to avoid foods containing saturated fat and foods containing a lot of sugar?				
Do you eat low-salt foods, avoid adding salt to cooking and eat meals without adding table salt?				
Do you drink 6–8 glasses of water a day?				
Do you always have breakfast?				

Use the information below to help you.

Fruit and vegetable servings

1 piece of fruit, e.g. an apple
2 tablespoons vegetables (cooked)
1 tablespoon dried fruit
1 glass of fruit juice

Starch

Bread   (preferably wholemeal)
Potato
Breakfast cereal (preferably wholegrain)
Rice (brown rice has more fibre than white)

Saturated fat

Poultry, pork and soya are lower in saturated fat.
Beef and lamb are higher in saturated fat.
Soya is a complete protein, so is a good substitute for vegetarians.
Eggs contain saturated fat.
Hard cheese such as cheddar is high in fat.
Semi-skimmed milk is less that 2% saturated fat, almost half as much as whole milk.
Butter and cream are saturated fat.
Vegetable, sunflower and olive oil are unsaturated, whereas lard is saturated.

Fish

Oily fish include salmon, mackerel, trout, herring, fresh tuna, sardines, pilchards, eels.
White (non-oily) fish include cod, haddock, plaice, coley, tinned tuna, skate, hake.

Salty foods

These include bacon, ham, some cheese, gravy granules, soy sauce.
High-salt foods are those which contain more than 1.5g salt per 100g (or 0.6g sodium).
Low-salt foods are those which contain 0.3g salt or less per 100g (or 0.1g sodium).

Sugary foods

High-sugar foods are those which contain more than 15g sugars per 100g.
Low-sugar foods are those which contain 5g sugars or less per 100g.

Compare your daily intake to the recommendations. Were there any surprises? If you identify that you are eating too much or too little of certain foods, use the table on the next page to plan a realistic one-day menu that fits in with the Food Standards Agency guidelines. Be realistic, don't include foods you don't like, or haven't time to cook. Try out your menu to see how easy it might be to change your diet. You can read more about Food Standards Agency guidelines on page 96.

Breakfast	
Lunch	
Dinner	
Snacks	
Drinks	

The Food Standards Agency has produced a book called 'Eat well, Your Guide to Healthy Eating' and a supporting CD-ROM which contains information on eating a healthy balanced diet. You can also access the information by going to http://www.eatwell.gov.uk.

The eatwell plate

Use the eatwell plate to help you get the balance right. It shows how much of what you eat should come from each food group.

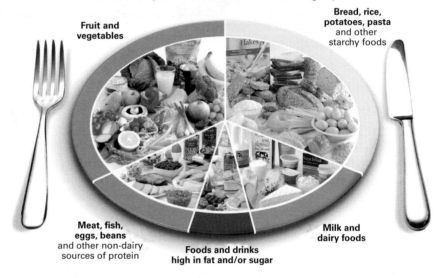

Source: The Food Standards Agency

Pregnancy and breastfeeding

Extra folic acid should be taken during the first three months of pregnancy, as this is recommended to prevent **spina bifida**. During the last 3 months of pregnancy a woman needs about an extra 200 calories a day. Whilst breastfeeding she will need an extra 500 calories. Extra calcium should be eaten, as the developing baby will take what it needs, leaving the mother short of what she needs. (This is why women often have to have more dental treatment during pregnancy and for the first year after having a baby.)

Pregnant women are advised to avoid certain foods that are known to be a potential risk to the unborn child. These include soft

spina bifida

a condition where the backbone is not properly formed, so that the nerves in the spine may be unprotected, and can cause bladder, bowel and mobility problems. In more severe cases there is loss of feeling from the waist down and blue vein cheeses, liver pâté, unwashed raw fruit and vegetables, raw or undercooked meat, unpasteurised goats' milk or goats' cheese, and liver. It is also recommended that pregnant women eat no more than four medium-sized tins of tuna per week, as tuna has been found to contain traces of mercury.

Older people (65+)

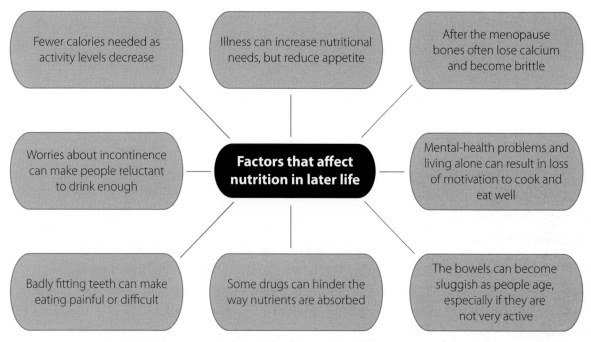

Fewer calories needed as activity levels decrease

Illness can increase nutritional needs, but reduce appetite

After the menopause bones often lose calcium and become brittle

Worries about incontinence can make people reluctant to drink enough

Factors that affect nutrition in later life

Mental-health problems and living alone can result in loss of motivation to cook and eat well

Badly fitting teeth can make eating painful or difficult

Some drugs can hinder the way nutrients are absorbed

The bowels can become sluggish as people age, especially if they are not very active

The dietary needs of older people do not change and they should follow the basic guidelines for a healthy diet in order to avoid poor nutrition

In the last 20 years or so, the concerns about poor **nutrition** in service users have begun to be highlighted. In August 2006 Age Concern published a report entitled 'Hungry to be Heard: The Scandal of Malnourished People in Hospital'. The report looked at statistics of the numbers of people, particularly elderly people, who become, or stay, malnourished in hospital. Several reasons were suggested, including:

- Insufficient help being offered to those who are unable to eat unaided.
- Staff failing to notice when patients were persistently leaving meals.
- Food being placed out of reach.
- Failure by staff to ensure individuals' preferences are taken into account.

You can access the report by going to www.ageconcern.org.uk; the Malnutrition Advisory Group also provides statistics on malnutrition in the community, see www.bapen.org.uk.

nutrition

a process that involves the intake, digestion and absorption of nutrients from food and drink

Similarly, the Royal College of Nursing, with the Nursing Standard, launched a campaign on 18 April 2007 entitled 'Nutrition Now', following a survey of over 2,000 nurses to find out the main barriers to helping patients to get good nutrition. The main reasons given were the lack of availability of food outside mealtimes and the lack of staff available to support patients during mealtimes, see www.rcn.org.uk.

The report suggests that it might not always be appropriate to follow the current recommendations for a healthy diet with older people. If an elderly person is eating insufficient amounts because they find food without salt tasteless, or much prefer butter to margarine, then less healthy food should be given. Similarly, someone who has a very poor appetite might not get enough calories if they are following a low-fat diet (Calverley, 2007).

Activity level

When trying to decide whether an elderly person is eating sufficient amounts of food, it is important to keep an eye on their weight. Monthly weighing should soon tell you if someone is starting to lose or gain a significant amount of weight, and action can be taken to rectify this. If a previously active person becomes immobile it is important that the calorific value of their food is reduced, but this does not mean they need to feel hungry. Semi-skimmed milk has only two-thirds of the calories of full-fat milk, for example, so this one change can reduce the daily calorie consumption by a useful amount.

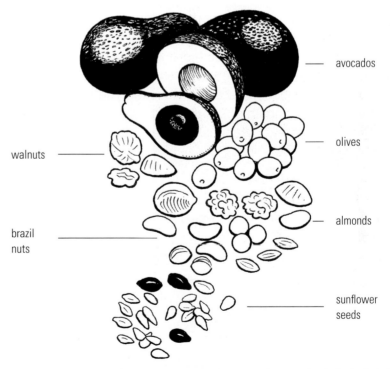

Eating plant foods is one way older people can ensure they are getting enough calories in their diet

If an elderly person is losing weight they are obviously not eating enough calories. This could be for a number of reasons, which are covered on page 56. The food they consume will need to be a good source of protein, vitamins and minerals. The highest-calorie foods are fats, but, of course, you cannot just feed elderly people on high-fat food, as it could raise their cholesterol levels. Plant foods such as nuts, seeds, olives, and avocados contain fats that are less harmful than animal fats, so these could be one solution.

Do beware of relying just on weight loss as a sign that someone isn't eating enough, as fluid retention, quite common in older people, will mask weight loss. Other ways of identifying unintentional weight loss are discussed on pages 56–7.

Lack of motivation

It is hard to remain enthusiastic about cooking for yourself when you live alone. If you live alone because your spouse has died, grief can add to the loneliness to further reduce motivation. It is easier to prepare a quick snack or rely on ready meals that create less washing-up. Grief can also lead to depression, which can cause loss of appetite and may result in poor nutritional status. Those particularly at risk are widowed men whose marriages were based on the traditional male/female roles, so that they never acquired the skills needed to provide themselves with a healthy diet.

Older widowed men who suddenly find themselves alone often lose the will to look after themselves, particularly in making sure they eat a healthy diet

Care scenario: Donald

Donald MacPherson is 75 years old. His wife died six months ago. They had been married for 53 years. His wife had always done the cooking. She died very suddenly after suffering a stroke. Donald was devastated. He misses her terribly. Even if he knew how to cook he just doesn't seem to have any appetite. He has lost 2 stone in weight since his wife's death.

If you were a care assistant visiting Donald, what would you do to try to rekindle his interest in food?

---

osteoporosis

a condition where the bones, particularly those of the spine, wrists and hips, become thin and weak, and break easily. Often there are no warning signs before a break occurs

Osteoporosis

It has been estimated that at the age of 50 years, 15% of women will have **osteoporosis**, 30% at the age of 70 and 40% at the age of 80. (Kanis et al, 1994). It is less common in men, but affects 1 in 12 at some time in their lives.

The inside of bone looks similar to a sponge. Throughout our lives old bone is continuously being broken down and replaced with new bone. Before about 25 to 30 years of age, bone is built up faster than it is broken down, after about 40 years of age the reverse is the case. When someone has osteoporosis the rate of destruction is such that bones become brittle and fracture easily, with the hips, wrists and spine being particularly at risk. This is known as osteoporosis.

Some people are more at risk than others, including those whose parents had osteoporosis, women who had the menopause before the age of 45, people who take steroids, and people with bowel disorders that affect food absorption. Lifestyle can also increase the risk of osteoporosis, particularly smoking or drinking too much alcohol.

It is not possible to increase your bone density after about 30 years of age, although there are measures that can be taken to slow the loss of calcium from the bones. A diet high in calcium and vitamin D and exposure to sunlight may help a little; of more importance is encouraging people with low bone density to do plenty of weight-bearing exercise, such as running, skipping, and brisk walking.

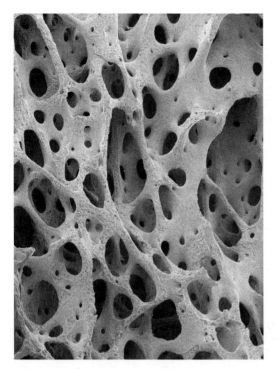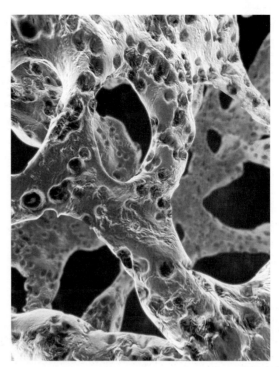

(Left) normal bone structure and (right) bone structure in osteoporosis. What can be done to slow down the loss of bone density and reduce the risk of osteoporosis?

Dehydration

Some elderly people do not seem to recognise the feeling of thirst. Others deliberately restrict their fluid intake, due to worries about **incontinence**. This can be especially true in the case of those taking diuretics ('water tablets'). In fact, restricting fluids can make incontinence worse, as urine is held in the bladder longer before the need to pass water is felt, increasing the risk of urinary tract infections, which themselves can lead to incontinence. Therefore, it is important to ensure that all elderly people drink the equivalent of at least eight large tumblers of fluid a day. This is even more important in summer months.

incontinence
passing urine when you don't mean to due to partial or total loss of control of the bladder

Dental problems

Any service user with poorly fitting dentures, few teeth or bad teeth is at risk of being poorly nourished. Chewing can be very difficult if your false teeth are loose. Decaying teeth may well be painful. If you have very few teeth it may be hard to eat foods that require a lot of chewing such as fruit, vegetables and meat.

Medication

Many prescription and non-prescription drugs can have a negative effect on the absorption of nutrients from the diet. For example aspirin, cimetidine, omeprazole and ibuprofen can all affect the absorption of iron, which could result in anaemia. Some drugs can cause nausea or loss of appetite.

Find out as many reasons as you can why service users might suffer from constipation.

What changes to the diet might help?

You can access information on the NHS Direct website: www.nhsdirect.nhs.uk.

Constipation

Difficulty with opening the bowels is called constipation. It is extremely common, particularly in older people, with women being affected more than men. Constipation can be caused by a number of factors, some of which are more common in elderly people. It is an uncomfortable condition and can be very distressing: some people seem to become obsessed about their bowels. Symptoms can include stomach ache, feeling bloated, feeling sick, headache, loss of appetite, and, particularly in older adults, confusion.

Activity 3

Give an example of one change you could make to a person's diet to improve their health and well-being in each of the situations below:

A teenager who has started to put on a lot of weight.	
A person who has been diagnosed with osteoporosis.	
An individual who is reluctant to drink.	
A man who lives alone and cannot be bothered to cook for himself.	
A woman who has badly fitting teeth and refuses to wear her new ones.	
A man who takes omeprazole to treat stomach ulcers.	
A toddler who always seems to be constipated.	

How culture can influence dietary choices

Activity 4

Create a day's menu that would be suitable for an elderly person.

Breakfast	
Lunch	
Dinner	
Snacks and drinks	

If you need to find out food sources of nutrients, look at Section 3.1

It is easy to assume that all elderly people enjoy old-fashioned dishes like tripe and onions. However, many elderly people enjoy a wide and varied menu, including many foods that have been introduced to the British menu over the last few decades. Some elderly people are traditional in their likes and dislikes, but it should not be assumed that all are.

Look back at your menu. Have you automatically assumed that an elderly person would eat traditional British foods, or have you included foods from other cultures?

You should be aware that many older people today eat a wider range of foods than the traditional British ones

Investigate the traditional diets of some cultures other than your own. If you discover any unfamiliar foods, try to find out what they are and how they are cooked and eaten.

halal

meat from an animal killed in accordance with Muslim ritual whereby it is bled to death

Of all the influences on a person's diet, culture is probably one of the greatest. In this context, culture does not necessarily mean religion. It means the environment in which you live, the foods that are commonly available, and the foods eaten at social occasions within your circle of friends and relatives. The eating habits we adopt are strongly influenced by the food our parents introduced to us in childhood and the foods we were introduced to by friends in early adulthood. Holidays abroad have been another influence on widening tastes. In Britain it is relatively easy to buy foods associated with a wide range of cultures.

How religion influences dietary choice

You need to find out how strictly your service users follow any religious restrictions. Whilst it is essential that you respect their religious beliefs, not everyone is strict. Occasionally you may encounter care staff who think that it doesn't matter if you give a person food that is against their religious beliefs, as long as they don't find out. This is totally unacceptable.

The table below shows the main dietary rules for six different religions.

Religion	Food restrictions	Preparation and handling
Islam	Muslims do not eat pork, or foods or medicines containing gelatin. No alcohol.	Meat must be **halal**.
Hinduism	Some Hindus are strictly vegetarian and do not eat eggs or seafood. Non-vegetarians do not eat beef. Alcohol is forbidden.	
Sikhism	Some Sikhs are strictly vegetarian and do not eat fish, eggs or animal fat. Non-vegetarians do not eat beef. Alcohol is forbidden.	Halal meat is not permitted.
Judaism	Meat must come from animals that have cloven hooves and chew the cud. Fish must have scales and fins. Poultry is acceptable. Milk and meat must not be eaten in the same meal.	Poultry, meat and animal fat and dairy produce must be kosher. Cheese must be certified by a rabbi. Meat and milk utensils, crockery and cutlery should be kept strictly separate, disposable cutlery can be used.
Buddhism	Many are vegetarian.	There are no rules about food preparation.
Christianity	Most eat meat but some are vegetarian. Some do not eat meat on Fridays and some fast during Lent, mainly for spiritual reasons.	There are no rules about food preparation.

Many religions include fasting at certain times (e.g. Islam during Ramadan – this is important and needs to be respected).

Activity 5

Esther Levy has just arrived at your care setting. It is lunchtime. She informs you that she is Jewish. Here is the menu; decide what would and would not be acceptable to offer her.

Starters	✓	✗
Tomato soup		
Prawn cocktail		
Egg mayonnaise		
Main course		
Roast chicken dinner		
Fish in parsley sauce with mashed potato and peas		
Vegetable curry and rice		
Dessert		
Fresh fruit salad		
Jelly and ice cream		
Baked apples		

More detail on kosher diets can be found by accessing http://www.unitedsynagogue.org.uk/jewish_living/keeping_kosher/keeping_kosher/what_is_kosher/

Medical conditions requiring special diets

Many medical conditions require service users to receive a special diet. The diet is vital to their well-being, and in some cases, serious consequences may follow if it is not kept to. Examples include:

- dysphagia
- diabetes mellitus
- coeliac disease
- kidney disease
- allergies
- gastrointestinal diseases.

Dysphagia

Dysphagia is a serious condition, and specialist training is required to safely care for a person with this condition. The information in this section is intended to help you to understand about dysphagia and special requirements of service users. If you have a person with dysphagia in your care, ask for further training or work under the direct supervision of someone who has received training.

dysphagia
difficulty in swallowing

The signs and symptoms of dysphagia can include any of the following:

- feeling as if food is stuck part way down
- weight loss
- pain on swallowing
- being unable to swallow at all
- choking on food
- heartburn
- vomiting.

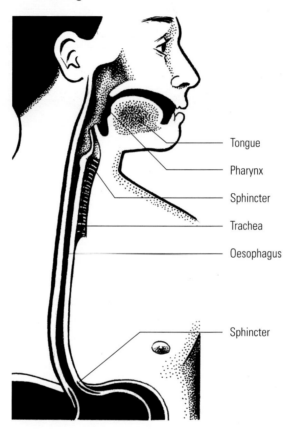

The digestive system. There are various physical, neurological and psychological causes that disrupt the digestive system and affect the diet of service users

When you swallow your tongue pushes the food that you have chewed to the back of your mouth. Muscles in your throat contract to move the bolus (ball of food) to the top of the oesophagus (gullet or food pipe). The food has to pass over the trachea (opening to the lungs), which should be protected by the epiglottis during swallowing to prevent food going 'the wrong way', which would cause choking. Muscles in the oesophagus push the food downwards. There is a sphincter muscle (circular band of muscle) at the top of the stomach, which opens every time you swallow, to let food pass into the stomach.

Causes

Dysphagia has a number of causes; they might be physical, neurological (nervous system disorders), or psychological.

The physical causes are:

- the sphincter at the top of the stomach doesn't open properly (achalasia), so food isn't entering the stomach
- the muscles in the oesophagus have become weak due to ageing
- a stricture (narrowing) of the oesophagus
- a tumour partially blocking the oesophagus
- something is stuck in the throat or oesophagus, such as a fish bone
- the oesophagus is inflamed or scarred due to frequent reflux of stomach contents back up into the oesophagus, perhaps due to a weak sphincter or a hiatus hernia
- a diverticulum (pouch) in the wall of the oesophagus.

The neurological causes are:

- stroke
- Parkinson's disease
- multiple sclerosis
- motor neurone disease
- dementia.

The swallowing difficulties associated with dementia include a delay in swallowing or failure to swallow something completely. Sometimes the person simply does not recognise that there is something in the mouth, and the food just sits there (http://dementia.ion.ucl.ac.uk).

The psychological causes are:

- stress
- tension
- fear.

For example, someone who is phobic about taking tablets may struggle to swallow them, even though they can swallow much larger boluses (lumps of food) without any difficulty. Giving tablets with milk can often ease difficulties in swallowing, but remember the advice on page 39.

Special diet for dysphagia

Food should be served soft for mild to moderate dysphagia, for example mashed potato, minced beef, and mashed swede. For more severe dysphagia a liquid diet can be given. A dietician would devise this, as it is important that the diet is **nutritionally balanced**. Sometimes a nasogastric tube is passed up the nose, down the back of the throat and into the stomach, so that a liquid diet can be given if swallowing is impossible.

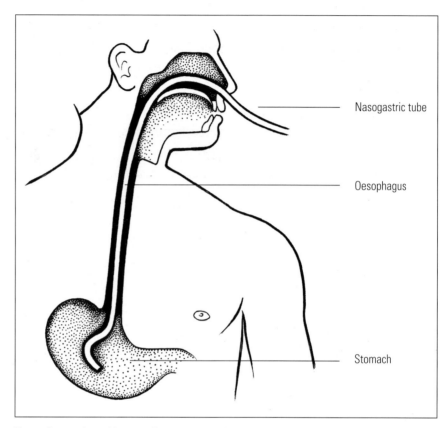

Nasogastric tube

Oesophagus

Stomach

If a service user is unable to swallow, a nasogastric tube may be inserted into the stomach to make this possible

In such cases feeds given must be specially prepared. They are called 'enteral feeds'. Standard enteral feeds contain all the carbohydrate, protein, fat, water, electrolytes, vitamins, minerals and fibre required. 'Pre-digested' feeds can be given to people who need to be able to absorb nutrients quickly, such as those with inflammatory bowel syndrome. Ordinary food that has been liquidised cannot be given, as this can cause infections and may block the nasogastric tube.

If the problem is likely to be long term a gastrostomy is often created. This is a tube that enters the stomach via the abdomen, thus avoiding the discomfort of a nasogastric tube. Sometimes this is known as **PEG feeding**. PEG stands for percutaneous endoscopic gastrostomy.

Children with gastrostomies often have a Mic-Key button rather than the gastrostomy illustrated above. A Mic-Key button is very neat, and lies flat on the abdomen.

Apart from people with dysphagia, other service users who may be fed through a gastrostomy include:

- patients on life support
- premature babies with a poor sucking reflex
- people with conditions such as cystic fibrosis or cancer, where the nutrition requirement is greater than the person is able to consume
- babies with congenital abnormalities of the oesophagus or mouth
- people who refuse essential specialised feeds, some of which taste horrible.

It is very important that individuals who receive nutrition through a tube do not feel isolated, as mealtimes are often a social occasion.

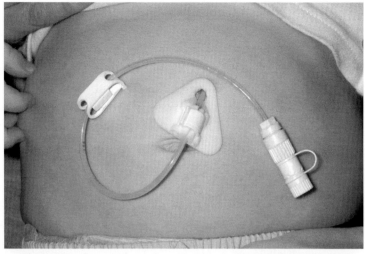

A gastrostomy may be used for someone who has a problem with swallowing food

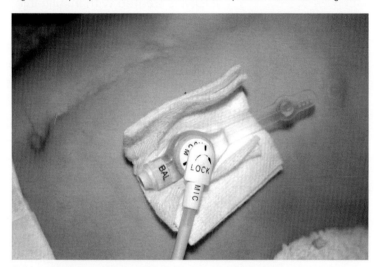

Children who have problems with swallowing may be fitted with a Mic-Key button rather than a gastrostomy

Children with nasogastric tubes, for example, can be given their feed at the table, and encouraged to play with feeding utensils to interact with other children at mealtimes. If they are able, some food can be taken orally.

Adults and older children may prefer to receive their feed in private, but could perhaps join other people at mealtimes, even if they are not receiving their feed at the time. You should be aware that for tube-fed adults, sharing mealtimes with others who are eating normally can have significant psychological effects. Offer choice and respect dignity and privacy at all times.

Imagine that one of your service users was being given tube feeds rather than eating normal meals. He or she would probably miss the social interaction that takes place at mealtimes. How could you prevent this person feeling isolated?

Diabetes mellitus

Diabetes mellitus is a condition where the hormone insulin is not being produced by the pancreas, or is being produced in insufficient quantities. Insulin is used by the body to move glucose from the blood into the cells where it is used for energy. There are two types of diabetes mellitus. If left untreated the most severe type would lead to certain death.

The most severe type is known as IDDM (insulin-dependent diabetes mellitus). It used to also be known as Type I diabetes, and this term may still be used.

The less severe form of diabetes mellitus is known as NIDDM (non-insulin dependent diabetes mellitus). It used to be known as Type II diabetes.

IDDM is treated with insulin injections, whereas NIDDM is treated either by diet alone or by a combination of diet and tablets.

Anyone with diabetes should see a registered dietician. A healthy diet is the key, as poorly controlled diabetes can lead to serious complications, including blindness, kidney failure, strokes, and gangrene, leading to amputation of lower limbs.

The aim of the diet is to control blood glucose, blood fats and blood pressure. Those with insulin-dependent diabetes mellitus should eat meals and snacks at regular times each day to keep a steady blood glucose level. If after being given insulin a person does not eat enough they may develop hypoglycaemia, or low blood sugar. This is because the insulin injection will remove a certain quantity of glucose from the bloodstream, so if insufficient has been eaten, the blood glucose level falls too low. People with diabetes should always have access to glucose to use in an emergency. For this reason many carry boiled sweets or sugar lumps with them. Symptoms of hypoglycaemia include confusion, unsteadiness, a fast pulse, shaking, sweating, headache and anxiety. Most diabetic service users will be able to recognise hypoglycaemia, but you may have people in your care who have dementia and diabetes. You will need to observe them closely to recognise hypoglycaemia.

Starchy foods such as porridge, chapattis, potatoes or wholemeal pasta are important for controlling blood glucose.

Saturated fats, such as butter, fat on meat and cream should be avoided. Vegetable oils, such as olive oil or sunflower oil, are much better. Cooking methods should be chosen to use less fat and oil, so serve grilled food rather than fried. Oily fish, such as salmon and tuna, is also an excellent source of healthy omega 3 fat. As with any healthy diet, five portions of fruit and vegetables should be included. Beans and pulses are very good for controlling blood glucose and fats.

Contrary to the advice given in the past, it is now recognised that sugar does not need to be entirely omitted, however it should only be taken in limited amounts. This is the same advice that is given to everyone.

As high blood pressure is a common complication of diabetes, a low-salt diet is important.

Alcohol can be drunk in moderation, but can cause hypoglycaemia if taken on an empty stomach along with insulin and some tablets for diabetes, so it is best avoided in such cases. It is important to know that excessive alcohol intake can cause hypoglycaemia. The effects of alcohol can mask the signs of hypoglycaemia.

During illness the liver sometimes produces glucose, so a person with diabetes will still need their insulin even if they are not eating. Blood glucose testing is crucial to monitoring the health of people with diabetes.

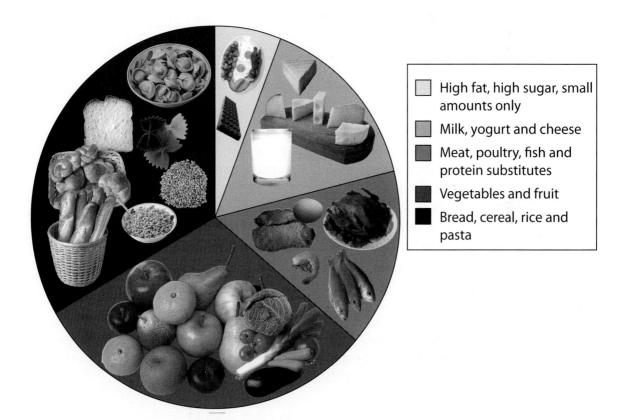

High fat, high sugar, small amounts only

Milk, yogurt and cheese

Meat, poultry, fish and protein substitutes

Vegetables and fruit

Bread, cereal, rice and pasta

The recommended diet for those with diabetes mellitus

Activity 6

Look at the guidelines for a diet suitable for a person with diabetes. Devise a menu for one day, taking all the guidelines into account.

Breakfast	
Mid-morning snack	
Lunch	
Mid-afternoon snack	
Dinner	
Supper	

food intolerance

a reaction to particular foods that does not involve an immune response. These can make you feel ill, but they are not usually harmful in the same way that a true food allergy might be. Such problems may be physical or psychological

Coeliac disease

This is an **intolerance** to the protein gluten, which is found in wheat, barley and rye. The gluten causes the immune system to produce antibodies, which attack the lining of the bowel. This can affect the body's ability to absorb nutrients from food, and can lead to anaemia and osteoporosis. It can also increase the risk of bowel cancer.

Some people are diagnosed in childhood, others not until much later, since the symptoms are similar to many other bowel disorders, and include abdominal pain – particularly after eating foods containing gluten – diarrhoea, constipation, bloating, failure to gain weight in childhood, weight loss in adulthood, and anaemia leading to tiredness.

Special diet

All foods containing wheat, rye and barley need to be avoided. This will include:

- bread, cake, biscuits, pasta, some breakfast cereals
- ready-made mustard, some mayonnaise, soy sauce, stock cubes
- beer, whisky
- sauces made using plain flour
- couscous.

Suitable foods that can be eaten include:

- fruit and vegetables
- potatoes, rice
- nuts
- meat and dairy products
- sauces made from cornflour.

Gluten-free breads, biscuits and cakes are available, but are very expensive to buy. If a person has been medically diagnosed with coeliac disease some gluten-free products can be obtained on prescription. Food lists are available from the Coeliac Disease society (see page 64 for contact details) or the British Dietetic Association, and some information is available on the Internet.

Activity 7

Next time you are at the supermarket, look at the range of foods available to customers who are intolerant to particular food components. It is useful to see what you can buy in case you ever need to get some at short notice. Compare the prices to other foods in the supermarket.

Other foods can cause similar problems in sensitive people. A common example is lactose, the natural sugar in milk. Children who are lactose intolerant have difficulty putting on weight and suffer from diarrhoea. Milk proteins are present in a wide variety of foods; lists of foods that are free from milk proteins are available from the British Dietetic Association.

Renal (kidney) disease

The kidneys get rid of waste products from protein (urea), which are passed out in urine. If they fail, urea builds up in the bloodstream. The kidneys can fail quickly (acute renal failure), for example in severe dehydration, or over a long time (chronic renal failure), for example as a complication of diabetes. Kidney function can also decline with age.

Each individual is different, so it is important that a dietician carries out an assessment and advises on diet. They may recommend caution with regard to protein, **phosphorus** and sodium.

If protein needs to be restricted you should watch the amount of meat, poultry, fish and dairy produce, soya and tofu given. You should not cut out protein altogether, as it is a vital part of the diet.

Foods high in phosphorus include dairy produce, beans, peas, pulses, nuts and drinks such as beer, cola and cocoa.

phosphorus

if phosphorus builds up in the body it can cause calcium to be lost from the bones, increasing the risk of fractures

Sodium should be restricted. Salt is sodium chloride, so should be restricted. 'LoSalt' is not suitable as a substitute, because it contains high levels of potassium. Some people may need a low-potassium diet and some may need reduced fluids. Everyone is different, so a registered dietician should recommend appropriate foods. Foods that are potentially high in sodium include bacon, ham, sausages, gravy mix, crisps, bread, breakfast cereals, soup and anything preserved in brine. Sodium may also be present in some medicines, especially effervescent (fizzy) soluble medicines. Salt should not be added in cooking or at the table.

Occasionally a low-potassium diet is recommended. Since many foods contain potassium, it is best to ask a dietician to advise on foods to avoid.

High potassium levels can cause cardiac arrest, which is when the heart suddenly stops. However, low potassium can cause the heart rate to slow down and weaken, and this can also lead to a cardiac arrest, so a dietician's advice is vital.

Fluids

Fluids are likely to be restricted when a service user is undergoing dialysis, and also in the final stages of renal (kidney) failure.

Fat

All renal patients are at an increased risk of developing heart disease, so should avoid saturated fat in their diet.

Allergies

Some service users have an allergy to particular foods. About one person in seventy is affected by allergies. Allergies should not be confused with food intolerances (see page 24), which may cause a variety of symptoms including bloating, abdominal pain and diarrhoea, but are not usually life-threatening. An allergic reaction can be severe and life-threatening.

Symptoms

Following contact with the allergy trigger food, the person will develop one or more of the following signs and symptoms within minutes or hours:

- itchy mouth
- swollen lips, mouth, tongue and/or throat
- rash (hives)
- wheezing
- vomiting and/or diarrhoea
- red itchy eyes.

Some people develop a severe reaction called anaphylactic shock. This is a rare but potentially fatal allergic reaction where symptoms develop all over the body, causing swelling, a rash (hives), loss of consciousness, low blood pressure and breathing problems. Every effort should be made to ensure that the service user is never given food containing the substance to which they are allergic. Anyone who is known to have a severe food allergy should be prescribed an Epipen, which they should carry with them at all times. An Epipen can quickly deliver adrenaline to lessen the symptoms. Both the allergic person and anyone who cares for them should be trained to use the Epipen.

In adults, the most common food **allergens** are nuts, fish and shellfish. In children cows' milk, eggs, soya, and wheat are common allergens, but any food can cause allergies in people who are sensitive to them.

Activity 8

Find out if anyone at your place of work is allergic to a particular food. Is there a system in place to warn new and agency staff so they do not accidentally give the allergen? Do all the staff know what to do if an allergic reaction takes place?

allergen

a substance that can cause an allergic reaction in a sensitive person when the immune system recognises it as foreign. Allergens cause no response at all in most people

Inflammatory bowel diseases

Inflammatory bowel disease (IBD) should not be confused with irritable bowel syndrome. IBD refers to two disorders, ulcerative colitis and Crohn's disease, which between them affect 1 in 400 people in the UK. Ulcerative colitis is an unpleasant disorder that causes ulcers in the wall of the rectum and the lower part of the large intestine. The person has an urgent need to open the bowels, often many times a day, and the stools are very loose and contain blood. This causes pain and tiredness. Crohn's disease can affect any part of the gut from the mouth to the anus, but commonly affects patches of the gut. The symptoms are very similar to ulcerative colitis: both have periodic flare-ups, and both are treated with medicines to reduce inflammation, and people with Crohn's disease may also be prescribed antibiotics. Both conditions may be treated surgically to remove damaged sections of intestine, and can require the formation of a stoma, either a colostomy or an ileostomy, which will mean that the person has to wear a bag attached to the outside of the abdomen.

A special diet is not particularly helpful for ulcerative colitis, but sufferers may benefit from a liquid feed that contains all the essential nutrients in a quickly digestible form, as is used for patients with Crohn's disease. This compensates for the loss of nutrients that results from the rapid speed with which food passes through the system. Individuals should avoid foods that make their symptoms worse, such as milk and other dairy produce, which can be particularly irritating to the bowel. Some people with Crohn's disease find a low-fibre diet helpful, in which case they should avoid foods such as wheat bran, fruit and vegetables. However, people with ulcerative colitis should have fibre in their diet.

Coronary heart disease

People who have coronary heart disease should eat a diet low in saturated fat. They should limit their intake of animal fats, such as the fat on meat, cream, butter and cheese. Eating a high-fibre diet has been shown to lower the cholesterol levels in the blood. Foods containing oats, for example porridge, are a particularly good source of fibre and have been shown to be effective in reducing cholesterol. This also applies to people who have high blood cholesterol levels but have not yet developed coronary heart disease. The recommended diet aims to reduce blood cholesterol. People with coronary heart disease often also have high blood pressure, so a low-salt diet is also important. People who are overweight should be encouraged to try to lose weight.

High-fat foods

Low-fat foods

It is vital that those suffering from coronary heart disease and those with high cholesterol levels and high blood pressure should know which foods to eat and which to avoid

Mental ill-health

Even without any physical cause, mental ill-health can have a significant impact on the diet. Obvious examples include anorexia nervosa and bulimia, but depression, **phobias**, and **dependency** can all affect nutritional intake. Early warning signs that someone is developing a mental-health problem can include anxiety, withdrawal, loss of confidence, being suspicious or saying things that don't make logical sense.

Anorexia nervosa

Anorexia means loss of appetite, which can have many causes, from bereavement to a medical disorder. **Anorexia nervosa** is an eating disorder affecting mainly girls or women, although boys or men can also be affected. It usually starts in the teenage years. The causes of anorexia nervosa are not really understood. It can affect more than one person in the same family. It can be associated with other mental-health conditions and it is commonly associated with perfectionists and people with low self-esteem.

The signs that indicate someone is developing anorexia nervosa may include obvious weight loss, avoidance of eating meals in the presence of others, an obsession about food, and dry, flaky skin, with a yellow tinge. Other signs and symptoms are harder to spot, as individuals tend to be very secretive about their condition. Efforts made to lose weight or maintain a very low body weight might include eating virtually nothing, exercising excessively, taking **laxatives** and diuretics, and deliberately vomiting.

People with anorexia nervosa often see themselves as being overweight, and have a fear of putting on weight.

The effects of their severely restricted diet include constipation, malnutrition, stomach ache, extreme tiredness, feeling bloated and feeling cold; females often stop having periods. Someone is said to be anorexic if they have a weight below 85% of the ideal for their height. Women with anorexia nervosa may find it more difficult to become pregnant, and are more likely to have premature or low birth-weight babies.

The treatment for people with anorexia nervosa extends beyond a special diet. Some people become so severely ill that they have to be admitted to specialist units for treatment, as the condition can be fatal.

...on that does not normally worry the majority of people

dependency

relying on something that is addictive, such as illegal drugs or alcohol

anorexia nervosa

is a serious illness, with a death rate of between 10% and 20%. The most frequent causes of death are starvation, dehydration, imbalance of electrolytes (essential minerals in the blood), infections, heart failure and suicide

laxative

medicine or tablet that causes a person to open their bowels

The aim of treatment is to restore healthy eating patterns and increase the body weight to a healthy level. In addition, **psychotherapy**, such as **cognitive behavioural therapy**, is used to allow patients to talk about their feelings towards food and to restore a healthier attitude to it.

Young people suffering from anorexia nervosa are at risk of damaging their physical and mental health

Bulimia nervosa

Bulimia nervosa is one of the most common eating disorders, characterised by periods of binge eating followed by vomiting, and in some cases, overuse of laxatives. Without treatment this 'binge and purge' cycle can lead to serious, long-term health problems. For example, acid in the mouth from vomiting can cause tooth decay due to damage to the tooth enamel, gum disease and/or irritation of the oesophagus. Any type of purging can lead to osteoporosis (see page 12), kidney damage, heart problems, or even death.

The physical symptoms of bulimia nervosa include:

- periods of weight loss and weight gain
- sore throat and loss of tooth enamel caused by stomach acid during repeated vomiting
- poor skin condition
- tiredness
- irregular periods
- bowel problems caused by overuse of laxatives.

It is thought to be a response to depression, low self-esteem or stress. Some people who develop bulimia may have been physically or sexually abused as children, while others may have been in difficult family or sexual relationships.

It can be difficult to notice bulimia nervosa initially, as the individual is not necessarily underweight. One sign to watch for is frequent vomiting, particularly after eating. There may be calluses or scratches on the knuckles if the person uses the fingers to make themselves vomit. Frequent vomiting can also cause bloodshot eyes. You may notice the person visiting the bathroom soon after every meal. Another sign might be that the person does an abnormal amount of exercise, and seems obsessed by this, even

psychotherapy

talking therapy used to help people with mental ill-health

cognitive behavioural therapy

therapy that helps people to replace negative thoughts and actions with positive ones exercising when ill. A person with bulimia may consider himself or herself to be overweight when they are not.

Treatment for bulimia involves a multidisciplinary approach. The team would include nurses, a dietician, a psychiatrist and therapists all contributing. The aim is to restore healthy eating patterns. Some people respond to medication, such as antidepressants.

Depression

People who are depressed often lose interest in everyday life. They can feel utterly incapable of doing anything, and this can include preparing meals or eating. Depression can affect decision-making skills, so individuals can find it hard to decide what food to buy. Confidence can be very low, meaning that a person does not trust their ability to do simple tasks such as cooking. Depression may also affect the appetite: some people lose their appetite, whilst others turn to food as a comfort.

Recent research from the Mental Health Foundation has shown that a healthy diet can have a positive impact on mental health. Advice suggests that the mood can be lifted by:

- eating regularly throughout the day
- choosing fewer refined high-sugar foods and drinks and more wholegrain cereals
- eating pulses, fruit and vegetables
- including protein at each meal
- eating a wide variety of foods
- including oily fish in their diet
- maintaining a healthy weight
- maintaining an adequate fluid intake
- keeping alcohol consumption within recommended limits
- exercising regularly.

(Harbottle 2007)

Dementia

In 2002 the University of Hull commissioned the Alzheimer's Society to carry out research into eating problems associated with dementia. The results, summarised below, were published in a report entitled 'Food for Thought'.

Many people with dementia lose interest in food, which can result in weight loss and this can lead to problems associated with poor nutrition, including a reduced ability to fight infections and anaemia. It is particularly important to make meals look appealing and to offer a portion that will not overwhelm the person. At the other extreme, some people start to eat a lot and begin to gain weight, which can lead to problems associated with obesity.

If an individual takes a long time to eat, an insulated plate can prevent their food from going cold too quickly. Encouraging the individual to help lay the table or prepare the food can reinforce that it is time to eat.

People with dementia sometimes find their tastes have changed, so they may reject foods they used to like, they may like unusual combinations and sweeter foods than they previously ate.

They can become distracted easily when eating and may need to be prompted to finish a meal; you may only have to place their cutlery back in their hands. When giving drinks, put the drink into the person's hand rather than leaving it on a table nearby. This should prompt them to drink it.

A service user who is prone to aggressive behaviour may physically resist attempts to assist them with eating. In this case it may be better to wait until they are calm before offering food again.

There may be safety worries when people with dementia still live at home. It is important to check food regularly to ensure that there is no out-of-date food in the fridge or larder. The ability to prepare food safely may be lost, increasing the risk of food poisoning. Some people with dementia eat non-food items by mistake, so anything that could be mistaken for food should be kept out of sight.

You can read more about eating problems associated with dementia at www.alzheimers.org.uk.

Substance dependency

People who are severely dependent on substances such as alcohol and drugs, can completely neglect their diet. In fact, people who drink large amounts of alcohol gain so many calories from drinking that they may lose their appetite. This will lead to malnutrition or deficiency diseases, such as iron-deficiency anaemia and beri-beri, which affects the heart and nervous system.

Phobias

There are different types of phobias associated with eating. One is fear of choking. Another is feeling or being sick just from smelling or seeing certain foods or feeling a certain texture in the mouth.

The person either responds by producing adrenaline as part of the 'fight or flight' response normally associated with danger, or is strongly repulsed by the food. Some people fear that food is contaminated and will make them ill, so will only eat food that has been prepared by certain people.

Care scenario: Margaret

Margaret Jackson is 78 years old. She was diagnosed with depression and paranoia 18 months ago, following a traumatic episode when her husband nearly died. Since then he has been unable to take his medication for severe arthritis, and has become severely disabled. Soon after her husband returned home from hospital she developed mental-health problems, resulting in her being hospitalized for 3 months. Since her discharge her condition has worsened, but she is so terrified of being readmitted to a psychiatric ward that she refuses all daycare or therapeutic care offered by the community psychiatric nurse (CPN). She now feels unable to cope with preparing all but the simplest of meals. The couple have meals-on-wheels delivered daily, but sometimes the food is **unpalatable**. If this is the case, Margaret will not eat much. The only other food eaten is cornflakes and marmalade sandwiches in the morning and cheese or ham sandwiches and cake in the evening. Margaret refuses to eat anything but white bread. She also thinks that the tap water is contaminated, and consequently drinks very little. As a result she is constipated and anaemic. She has lost 3 stone in weight.

This illustrates how difficult it can be to maintain good nutrition, as Margaret is not ill enough to have care forced on her.

1. Why do you think Margaret is anaemic and constipated?
2. If you were Margaret's care assistant, what would you do to try to improve her diet?
3. Give two examples of situations you would report to Margaret's doctor or CPN that you think would be too unsafe to leave without reporting.
4. How do you feel about the practice of allowing people with mental ill-health to refuse treatment and care as long as they are not in actual danger, and are not endangering others?

The effects of disability on food and nutrition

Physical disability

Physical disability can have various effects on an individual's ability to provide adequate nutrition. Some people with a physical disability find shopping difficult or impossible due to immobility or an inability to carry heavy shopping home, meaning they have to rely on others to select foods for them. This could result in shoppers choosing less healthy products, or being less choosy when selecting vegetables and meat. There could be difficulties in the cooking process, because the cooker hob is too high, or lack of the physical strength needed to lift pans and pour liquids. Another problem could be an inability to hold or control cutlery due to, for example, cerebral palsy, a stroke, or motor neurone disease. Aids and adaptations are covered in section 1.3.

Learning disability

A learning disability is a permanent condition usually resulting from the way the brain develops before or after birth. Or it may be a result of an inherited condition, an infection or a brain injury. A

> **unpalatable**
> *not pleasing to the taste*

learning disability affects the way in which a person learns, which includes learning to carry out everyday tasks. People with a learning disability will need extra support in learning how to plan and prepare meals, from choosing a menu to cooking and clearing away.

Some people with a learning disability may only eat a limited range of foods. An example is someone who will only eat foods that don't need to be chewed. Some people will only eat in a specific place, at a specific time or only certain favourite foods, or will not eat foods of a certain colour. This is sometimes seen in people with autism.

Some people with a learning disability may not be able to distinguish between what is edible and what is not. This can be particularly problematic for those who have lived in long-stay institutions and have never seen food in its unprepared state, or people with a severe learning disability who cannot distinguish inedible parts of foods, such as bone, eggshells and onion skin, from edible parts (see F. Bryan, T. Allen, L. Russell, 2000).

Everyone should be offered a choice at mealtimes. People who are not able to talk should be enabled to express a preference either by pointing at the menu, or the food, or a picture of the food they would like. This includes people on a special diet.

Activity 9

Create a pictorial menu that could be used to allow a person with communication difficulties to make a choice. Alternatively, learn some British Sign Language or **Makaton** signs associated with food and drink, so you could offer and understand choices when caring for people for whom this is their only form of communication. See http://www.rnid.org.uk/information_resources/communicating_better/bsl_video_clips/

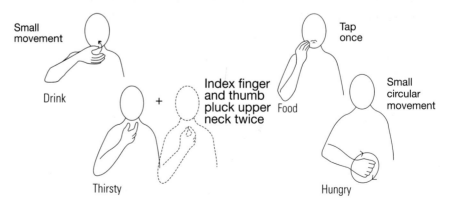

The Makaton symbols enable service users to communicate about the food and drink they want and when they want it

Timing and availability of food and drink

The timing of meals can be relevant to several things. Some medications need to be given with foods, others before or after food. The effectiveness of medications can be reduced if they are given at the wrong time.

Mealtimes are an important part of the day for service users and something people look forward to. If possible, mealtimes should not be interrupted unless this cannot be avoided. Sometimes people have to attend appointments over a mealtime. It is important that a meal is available for them on their return, otherwise they will be hungry. It may be that a service user wishes to have their mealtime arranged around a favourite TV programme. For those who are physically impaired TV can be one of their main pleasures in life, so it is not necessarily an unreasonable request.

When people are ill, they do not necessarily want to eat at specified times. For example, people on chemotherapy may only have certain times when they do not feel nauseous. Children might only eat when parents are present. It is therefore important that food is available at times other than mealtimes. Practically, this is unlikely to be a full meal, but even if it is only soup, toast or sandwiches, it means that service users are not left hungry.

The 'Better Hospital Food' programme was introduced during 2001, and included the requirement for hospital wards to introduce Protected Mealtimes. During protected mealtimes, non-urgent treatments, such as blood tests, x-rays and wound dressings are not allowed to disturb patients from eating their meals. The initiative also recommended the introduction of 24-hour catering, meaning that patients should be able to ask for hot food, snacks and drinks at any time of the day or night. In practice, however, most hospitals have not implemented this.

The National Minimum Standards for Care Homes for Older People (see pages 118–19) require that relatives, and service users themselves, should have access to cooking facilities.

Drinks should be readily available. Water should be available at all times, perhaps by leaving jugs of water for service users to help themselves. People who are too ill or infirm to do this should be offered drinks frequently, especially in hot weather.

For those who live in their own home, but who are unable to cook or shop independently, planning is needed to ensure that food and drink are available when needed and desired. Lunches can usually be provided by the local meals service, which is organised through social services. Hot meals are delivered daily, even at weekends in cases where there is no realistic alternative. Some local authorities provide a choice of meals, which must be ordered in advance; others will just deliver meals without offering a choice. Special diets will be catered for. If the meal arrives too early, it can be kept hot in the oven, although this will reduce its nutritional value as vitamin levels soon start to drop as food is kept hot. The food should be kept above 63°C to prevent food poisoning (Food Standards Agency, 2005). If food is being reheated after being allowed to cool, it must be piping hot all the way through. To be safe, you should use a temperature probe to check that food is properly reheated.

For those who can manage to cook ready meals, private companies and some local authorities provide an alternative service. However, meals usually have to be ordered on a weekly basis, so this option may be unsuitable for those who are confused or have mental-health problems. This means that these individuals do not get the added benefit of a person calling daily, and who would be able to raise the alarm if the service user was ill, or if entry could not be gained to a house that was normally unlocked.

Each person is different, so when choosing who will provide meals, the pros and cons of each system need to be considered.

For other meals, service users may be able to manage independently as long as the food is in the house. Shopping can be done by a home-care assistant, a relative, a neighbour or by ordering on the Internet. For those who cannot prepare any meals independently, a home-care assistant, relative or neighbour might help. If a cooked lunch is required, many service users will be happy with a flask of hot drink or soup, and a light meal left in the fridge, covered to keep it fresh.

Personal choice

Most people have likes and dislikes in foods, and very few like absolutely every food that is offered to them. Some people feel it is morally wrong to eat animals, and therefore wish to follow a **vegetarian** diet. Some people extend this to a vegan diet, where no animal products are eaten at all. Religion can also impose restrictions on dietary intake (see page 16). When providing food and drink to service users these considerations need to be taken into account, as you also need to ensure that the diet provided is nutritionally balanced. It is not satisfactory to serve the same meal to everyone, omitting the foods that are not wanted: something of equal nutritional value must be substituted.

vegetarian

someone who eats no meat or fish and sometimes no animal products at all. There are sub-categories of vegetarianism depending upon what is excluded from their diet

1. In what ways do nutritional requirements change as we age?

2. What factors can affect an elderly person's ability to maintain a nutritious diet?

3. What do you need to remember when you have service users who require a special diet?

4. What happens in your care establishment if a meal arrives and the service user is not ready to eat?

5. If meals on wheels arrive very early, how can they safely be kept hot until the individual is ready to eat?

In this section you are going to learn why the presentation of food and drink is so important. This includes prevention of food poisoning as well as ensuring that service users enjoy their food, eat a nutritious diet, and get enough to eat and drink.

Henryk Krygowski is 85 years old. He fought in the Second World War and settled in Peterborough in 1946. He has Parkinson's disease and dementia. His wife, Mary, was unable to manage him at home as he is incontinent and can be aggressive, so he moved into a residential home two months ago.

Mary visits Henryk every day. She often arrives at lunchtime, and finds his lunch untouched. When Mary offers him food, he takes it hungrily and, more worryingly, he drinks thirstily from the beaker, when she offers it.

See pages 31–2 for more information about dementia.

What you need to learn

- Food hygiene.
- Personal hygiene.
- Consistency and texture of food and drink.
- Temperature of food and drink.
- Variety.
- Attractive appearance of food and drink.
- Portion size.
- Supplementary and complementary foods.
- Reconstitution and moulding of foods.
- Enabling individuals to prepare their own food as appropriate.
- Food and hospital care.

Food hygiene

It is essential when preparing and serving food for anyone that you practise strict food hygiene to prevent food poisoning. There is more detail on food hygiene in section 2.3 (pages 67–75).

Personal hygiene (worker and individual)

Essential to good food hygiene is good personal hygiene, as one of the main ways food can become contaminated is through touch. Remember to wash your hands and those of the service users before dealing with food, and whenever your hands may have become contaminated with germs, such as after using the toilet. Clean clothing covered with an apron, which should be changed frequently, is also important to ensure that germs are not transported on clothes. This topic is discussed in more detail in section 2.3 (pages 65–7).

Consistency and texture

Consistency is a matter of how soft or hard the food is. Food can also be presented in liquid form, so consistency in this case would mean how runny or thick the food was. Special liquid food is used for tube feeding (see pages 20–1). A soft diet includes only easily chewed foods, so it might be recommended for people who have few or loose teeth. Food might be presented as a thickened liquid or a purée for people with swallowing difficulties. Care must be taken to ensure that such a diet is nutritionally adequate.

If a service user has been assessed by a dietician as needing a diet of a particular consistency, this must apply to everything,

> **consistency**
> *the degree of thickness or firmness of the food*

including drinks given with medication, and medication itself. A soft diet may only apply to food; if so, drinks can be of normal consistency. It would be useful for the dietician to leave a description of how thick the food and drink should be to help staff check that the consistency is correct.

The British Dietetic Association suggests categorising foods in a similar way to the table below:

Consistency	Examples
Thin fluid	Water, fruit squash
Naturally thick fluid	Full-fat milk, Complan® made up according to instructions
*Thickened fluid, stage 1	Coats back of spoon, can be drunk through a straw
*Thickened fluid, stage 2	Can be drunk from a cup, but not through a straw
*Thickened fluid, stage 3	Needs to be taken from a spoon
Smooth pouring	Thin custard, smooth tomato soup
Smooth purée	Thick custard, puréed apple, smooth yogurt
Smooth mouldable	Mousse, smooth fromage frais, creamed potato
Soft variable texture	Fruit yogurt, flaked fish, mashed potato
Tender, easily chewable	Chicken, carrot, swede, banana, avoid choking hazards
Normal	Any foods

* Fluid thickened with a commercial thickener

People who eat a liquid or very soft diet are more likely to develop problems with constipation or diarrhoea, and this will be need to be discussed between the dietician and staff responsible for preparing the meals.

Some people don't like the sensation of certain **textures** in their mouths, such as sloppy foods.

The texture of food is sensed by the tongue and palate. Different textures include crispy, crunchy, chewy, smooth, tender, slimy, gelatinous, powdery, and stringy. Stringy foods can get trapped in between the teeth, causing gum inflammation and halitosis (bad breath), unless good oral hygiene is maintained. They can also be a choking hazard.

Individual preferences should be considered when serving food, for example service users should be asked whether they want gravy, and if so, how much and where they would like it.

texture
the feeling of food in the mouth

Temperature

It is important to ensure that meals are served at an appropriate temperature. Hot meals and drinks should be given to service users before they have gone cold. Care must be taken to ensure that you are not risking service users scalding their mouths. If helping someone to take a hot drink, do not tip the beaker too much. If a hot meal is left to go cold, it is likely that the service user will lose interest in it. If an individual is unable to eat unaided, a carer should start to help them straight away. If no one is available to help, then the food should be kept hot until a carer is available. If the service user takes a long time to eat, an insulated plate could be used to keep the meal warm for longer.

It is equally important that foods intended to be eaten cold, such as ice cream, should be offered before they have melted. Most people prefer cold drinks to be cold rather than at room temperature, so water jugs should be filled just before a meal starts.

A carer may have to help a service user who has particular difficulties in eating their food

Variety

A varied diet is important to ensure that all the essential nutrients are included in the food we eat. The variety of food readily available to the British population is very wide. Some people like a wide range of foods, while others tend to stick to a few familiar foods. In the absence of particular disorders, vitamin and mineral supplements should not be needed if a varied diet is eaten. Those who have a very restricted diet may be lacking in vital nutrients, particularly vitamins and minerals, so in these circumstances it might be necessary to assess the diet and consider whether particular supplements need to be given. In this case advice will be needed from a dietician.

Care scenario: Unbalanced diets

We all need a varied diet in order to obtain all the nutrients our bodies need to maintain organs, tissues and cells, and to support development and growth. Our daily food intake should provide sufficient resources to support growth and activity, and should include a balance of protein, carbohydrate, fat, minerals and vitamins (see pages 4–11)

Any diet that includes far too much, or too little, of the essential nutrients can lead to a number of health problems including anaemia, heart disease, obesity, poor nerve function and problems with bone and muscle.

Eating a healthy diet, like many things, is learned in childhood, so children should be encouraged to eat as wide a range of foods as possible. Falling into the habit of eating a very restricted diet can have serious effects on their growth and development.

In February 2005 the BBC reported about 15-year-old Craig Flatman, whose diet consisted almost entirely of jam sandwiches. You can access the BBC report at http://www.bbc.co.uk/insideout/east/series7/jam_sandwich_diet.shtml

Attractive appearance of food and drink

One important way of tempting people to eat the meals you offer them is to make them look attractive. Colour is very important to the attractiveness of a plate of food. The addition of green vegetables, for example, makes a meal look far more appetising than having similar-coloured foods on the same plate. It is also important that the food looks tasty. Many people do not like greasy food, so take care to offer lean meat, and do not serve greasy gravy. Food should be nicely arranged on the plate.

Activity 10

There are many books about healthy food for children, some of which show meals presented in a fun way. If you have access to children, experiment with giving them the same meal, once set out in a normal way, and then again in a similar way to the picture below. Decide whether setting the meal out differently had any effect on the amount of food that was eaten.

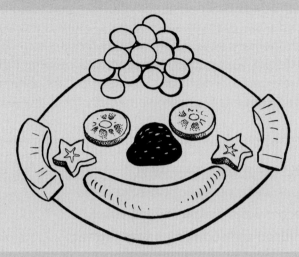

Portion size

A person who is ill may not have a very good appetite. It is therefore important to offer small portions, as people who are not very hungry can be overwhelmed by a large plateful of food and may end up eating less. However, some **individuals**, such as young male patients who are injured rather than ill, may need large portions of food to satisfy their appetites. People should be consulted about how much food they want, as only they know how much they normally eat. Some people may not be able to eat enough in a single meal, and smaller, more frequent meals or snacks may meet their needs better.

individual

the person receiving care and support

Supplementary and complementary foods

If a dietician feels that an individual's diet is lacking in certain nutrients, then **supplementary foods** should be given to try to address this. This might be in the form of tablets, such as iron tablets, or adding foods rich in the missing nutrients to the diet. For example you might sprinkle bran onto porridge to increase fibre intake. If this is not sufficient, then **complementary foods** such as Complan® or Build-up might be offered as a source of protein, carbohydrates, vitamins and minerals. There is a wide variety of supplementary and complementary foods, each designed for different deficiencies. It is therefore important that individuals are referred to a dietician. Some people are particularly likely to need supplementary or complementary food, including those:

- who have lost their appetite
- who are ill or recovering from an operation
- who have poor teeth, or cannot eat solid food
- who have recently lost weight unintentionally
- who are confused and sometimes forget to eat.

Information about PEG feeding can be read in Section 1.1 (see page 20).

Reconstitution and moulding of food

If a person has difficulty chewing, their food may have to be puréed. It can look very unappetising, so some hospital catering departments have developed a way of moulding puréed foods to make them look more appealing. For example, puréed chicken is moulded into a shape that resembles a chicken breast, and puréed potatoes are served to look similar to mashed potato. The puréed foods are made more nutritious by adding supplements or milk powders. Patients have been encouraged to comment on their enjoyment of these foods, and the results have shown that patients enjoy their meals more, and are more likely to eat the whole meal (www.dietetics.co.uk).

Enabling individuals to prepare their own food as appropriate

Any service user who is able should be allowed and encouraged to prepare their own food and drink, wherever possible. For some service user groups, mainly those with learning disabilities, physical disabilities and mental ill-health, this should be the norm.

The National Minimum Standards for Care Homes for Older People state that older people should have the opportunity to participate in preparing food for themselves if they wish. They recognise that health and safety restrictions may prevent service users using the main kitchen, but suggest that care settings can provide kitchenettes, or organise cooking activities for residents. Of course, one of the reasons why a person may opt for residential care is so as not to have to worry about cooking, so not all service users will wish to participate.

Service users with learning disabilities may need support through the whole process, from deciding what they are going to eat and being encouraged to choose a healthy diet, to buying ingredients and preparing meals in a safe and hygienic manner.

People with physical disabilities may need aids to help with food preparation, such as non-slip mats to enable one-handed stirring (illustrated on page 82). They would also benefit from someone accompanying them to the shop, and reaching items from the shelves. The kitchen may need adapting, with lower work surfaces, easy-turn taps and waist-high cupboards and oven.

The difficulties associated with food preparation for those with mental ill-health can be quite different. They may find it hard to motivate themselves to cook at all, or find leaving the house to go shopping difficult. Their appetite might be poor, or they might have difficulty knowing what to do with waste food.

Care scenario: Patrick, Anthony and Hanif

Patrick O'Brien is 22 years old. He has learning disabilities, and has just moved into a house with two friends, Anthony and Hanif, who also have learning disabilities. All three can read simple words, but find complex words difficult. They want to be as independent as possible.

Jonathan Bryce works for the Learning Disability Support Unit with the local authority. He has been allocated to work with Patrick, Anthony and Hanif as their community support worker.

How should Jonathan support these three young men to encourage independence whilst keeping them safe and well?

Food and hospital care

There has been much criticism of the quality of food served in hospitals in recent years. There are however several factors other than food quality which may have a negative effect on the dietary intake of people in hospital:

- loss of appetite is a common symptom of ill-health
- communication difficulties may make it hard to state what food you like or fancy
- being in a ward with other people who might be vomiting or suffer from incontinence can put patients off eating.

In addition to these factors the following may further discourage patients from eating:

- poor menu choice, perhaps only one option for those requiring a special diet
- poor presentation of meals
- meals arrive overcooked and/or lukewarm
- insufficient staff to help people who cannot eat independently
- inappropriate portion sizes provided
- patients being taken off the ward for investigations over mealtimes, although this should not happen with the Protected Meal Times initiative.

In October 2006 the Commission for **Patient and Public Involvement (PPI) Forums** carried out a survey into the quality of hospital meals as part of the 'Food Watch' campaign.

The survey discovered that:

- almost half the patients (40%) had their hospital meals supplemented by food brought in by visitors (this went up to 42% in community hospitals and 44% in specialist hospitals)
- over a third of patients (37%) left their meal because it looked, smelt or tasted unappetising
- over a quarter of patients (26%) are not receiving the help they need to eat their meals (this went up to almost a third in general hospitals)
- over 22% were given meals that were not warm enough or too hot
- almost a fifth of patients (18%) didn't get the choice of meal they wanted.

You can access the survey by going to http://www.cppih.org.

Patient and Public Involvement (PPI) Forums

these are made up of local volunteers who are enthusiastic about influencing and improving the way that local healthcare is delivered

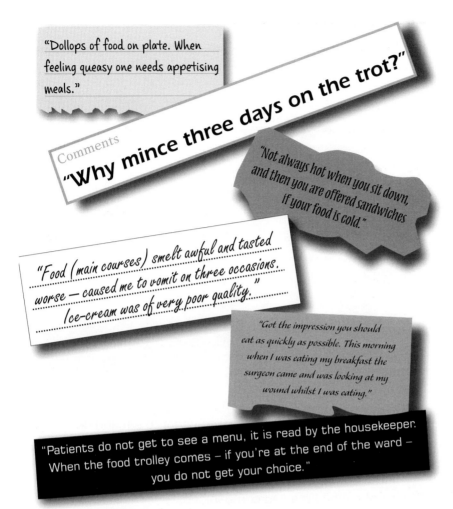

"Dollops of food on plate. When feeling queasy one needs appetising meals."

Comments

"Why mince three days on the trot?"

"Not always hot when you sit down, and then you are offered sandwiches if your food is cold."

"Food (main courses) smelt awful and tasted worse – caused me to vomit on three occasions. Ice-cream was of very poor quality."

"Got the impression you should eat as quickly as possible. This morning when I was eating my breakfast the surgeon came and was looking at my wound whilst I was eating."

"Patients do not get to see a menu, it is read by the housekeeper. When the food trolley comes – if you're at the end of the ward – you do not get your choice."

Samples of comments made by service users about the quality of hospital food they received

Activity 11

Look at the comments researchers from the Public and Patient Involvement Forum received when carrying out their survey on hospital food. Devise some basic rules for providing meals to hospital patients, to ensure that they receive adequate nutrition during their stay in hospital.

1. How can presentation of food affect the dietary intake of service users?

2. When should you wash your hands when handling food and drink?

3. Give three reasons why you would serve soft food to service users.

4. Why should you not liquidise ordinary food to use for feeding service users with gastrostomies or nasogastric tubes?

5. Why should you encourage service users to prepare their own meals, if they are able to?

In this section you will learn the importance of the surroundings and atmosphere to encourage service users to eat and drink well.

What you need to learn

- Choice of eating area and companions.
- Positioning and support of individuals to aid swallowing, digestion and general comfort.
- An attractive and clean environment.
- Aids to facilitate eating and drinking.
- In a residential setting, use a restaurant-style layout and serve one table at a time.
- Position of worker if assisting an individual with eating and drinking.
- Ensure that individuals are not rushed with their meals.

Choice of eating area and companions

It is common practice to encourage all residents in a setting to sit in the dining room together to have meals, sitting at tables with two or three other service users. This makes mealtimes a social occasion. There may be times when this is not the preference of individuals, and you need to be aware of this and respond to individual needs. Some people may feel embarrassed about eating in front of others, especially if they find it difficult to eat without spilling food, or if they have trouble keeping all the food in their mouth. This can happen if a person has cerebral palsy or has had a stroke, for example. Some service users do not like to sit at a table with others who have this type of difficulty, as it puts them off their own food. We are so concerned about inclusiveness that it is almost seen as unacceptable to express this, for fear of seeming rude or uncaring, but it could be a real concern. If someone asks to eat in their own room, you should try to find out why. As long as it has been determined that the person is not isolating themselves due to depression or because they wish to dispose of their food rather than eating it, then the request should be granted.

Positioning and support of individuals to aid swallowing, digestion and general comfort

You know from personal experience that it is much easier to eat sitting up than lying down. Eating whilst lying down increases the risk of choking, reflux, indigestion and aspiration pneumonia, as well as spilling food. It is therefore important that, unless otherwise indicated, you sit people well up before starting to help them with their meal, or before they start to eat. Many frail people slip gradually down their bed or chair during the course of the day, so you need to ensure that they are well supported.

If sitting at a table, service users should be well supported and positioned close to the table with everything they need to hand.

At home you probably don't always eat your meal at a dining table. If there is something you want to watch on television you might have your meal on a tray on your knee. In nice weather you probably enjoy eating in your garden or going for a picnic. Service users are no different. How easy would it be to serve meals elsewhere? Could you take your service users on a picnic?

Service users who should not be moved into an upright position include those being nursed flat due to back injuries, meningitis or following certain anaesthetics, such as an epidural.

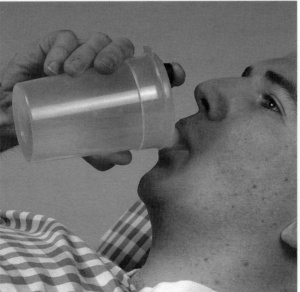

A feeding cup controls the flow of drinks and so is suitable for service users who are unable to sit up. Remember that the liquid at the bottom is drunk first, so don't use tea leaves!

An attractive and clean environment

An attractive table adds to the enjoyment of a meal. A table should be laid properly using a tablecloth; a small vase of flowers will brighten its appearance.

1. The plate is always in the centre of the place setting.
2. The cutlery is set out in the order it will be used, with the cutlery to be used first on the outside.
3. The side plate is positioned to the left of the forks, the tea knife is placed on the side plate.
4. The napkin is placed to the left of the fork, with the fold on the left. It can also go under a fork, or on top of the plate.
5. The knives are placed to the right of the plate with the sharp blade facing in towards the plate.
6. If a soup spoon is needed, it is placed to the right of the knives.
7. The drinking glass is placed at the tip of the knife.
8. The cup or mug is placed to the top right of the spoons.

Service users should have the opportunity to wash their hands before eating. They should be comfortably seated and able to reach whatever they need on the table.

Aids to facilitate eating and drinking

It is desirable to help people to remain independent with eating for as long as possible, as it raises their self-esteem. It also means they can eat as soon as the meal arrives, without having to wait for help. There are a variety of aids available to assist service users to eat independently.

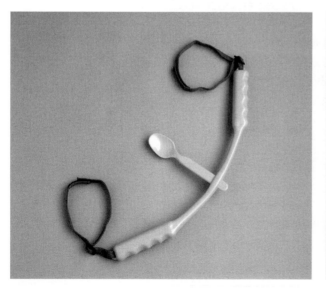

What kinds of problems do you think these items could help with?

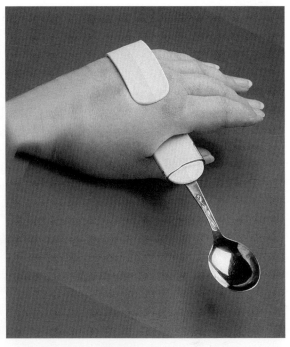

A plate guard can be used on any plate to prevent food spills

This gadget enables independent eating in those unable to grip cutlery

In a residential setting, use a restaurant-style layout and serve one table at a time

Setting out the dining room in restaurant style has several benefits for staff and service users. Sitting several people at one table makes the meal a more sociable occasion. They can all be served together, reinforcing table etiquette, such as the custom of waiting for everyone's meal to arrive before starting to eat. This might not be relevant to older people, who may find it patronising, however some service-user groups, for example children, are still learning social skills, so it may be appropriate to encourage table manners. Tables arranged in this way make it easier for staff to walk around to serve people and to offer help. It might be helpful to put those who eat at a similar speed at the same table, so that there is less delay serving the next course. You might also group people with friends, or those of similar interests, or use it as an opportunity to sit someone next to someone they don't know very well so that they can get to know them better. This may not be possible in a hospital setting, especially on an acute ward.

Position of worker if assisting an individual with eating and drinking

When you are helping someone to eat or drink, you should sit down facing them, or at slight angle to them. This will ensure that you don't look as though you are trying to rush them. If you stand beside someone to help them with their meal, it gives the impression that you haven't got much time, and they may, through embarrassment, say they have finished before they really have. It is better for the care worker's physical well-being to sit with their back supported rather than standing and bending over. It is also an opportunity to chat to the service user. If possible, one carer should be assigned to help each service user, so you can give them your full attention.

Ensure that individuals are not rushed through their meals

People who need help with eating are often slow eaters. The disability or impairment that prevents them from being able to eat unaided, may also mean that chewing and swallowing are difficult. Wait until a mouthful has been swallowed before putting more food into the mouth. Resist the temptation to ask someone if they are ready for more food when they clearly still have food in their mouth. Doing this will make them self-conscious about their slowness in eating, and think that you resent the time it takes to help them. Do not put too much food in the mouth at a time, and offer drinks frequently to keep the mouth moist, especially with dry foods. Ask if they would like a short break between courses, but do not forget to go back to them.

1. Give an example of a factor in the environment where meals are being served that might put people off their food.

2. How should you position a service user at the beginning of a meal?

3. Describe two aids that could enable service users to be more independent in eating and drinking.

4. Write a list of guidelines you could give to care workers to ensure that service users who are unable to eat unaided can enjoy their meals.

Roles and boundaries

2.1 Understand the role, responsibilities and boundaries of the worker with regard to following the policies and procedures of the care setting on assessment of dietary requirements

In this section you will learn your role, and the limits of your role, in the policies and procedures regarding diet and nutrition of the people for whom you care.

What you need to learn

- Person-centred approach.
- Nutritional screening.
- Care planning.
- Risk assessment.
- Oral health.

Person-centred approach

person-centred approach

an approach to care planning and support that places the person at the centre of care, enabling them to take part in making decisions about their care

The phrase '**person-centred approach**' involves putting the service user at the heart of your work, so that everything is planned around their needs, rather than, for example, the convenience of the staff or the efficiency of the organisation. Meals are a central part of the care of service users. For some they are one of life's main pleasures and one of the most enjoyable parts of the day. You should make a special effort to give service users food that they enjoy, as long as it isn't doing them any harm. If they are terminally ill, then it may be wholly appropriate to give food that isn't healthy, if that is what they want. It may sometimes be more important to ensure that people eat something rather than nothing, whether it is healthy or not.

If a service user is malnourished or requires a special diet, they should still be given a choice of meals, and their needs and preferences must be taken into account. As a care worker it is your role to do everything you can to ensure that your service users enjoy their food. It may be that the cook plans the meals and the manager dictates the budget, but you may be able to pass on suggestions of favourite meals and recipes from service users. If there is a service users' group at your workplace, meals could be an agenda item.

There should be access to drinks at all times, and it should be possible to provide light snacks if service users have missed a meal for some reason.

Nutritional screening

In the UK malnutrition often remains undetected and untreated and costs the NHS over £7.3 billion a year. Malnutrition can include undernutrition, which is a deficiency of calories or of one or more essential nutrients. It can also refer to overnutrition, which results from eating too much, eating too many of the wrong things, not taking enough exercise, or taking too many vitamins or other dietary replacements.

Very little information is available about how common undernutrition is in children, but available records suggest that 5% of pre-school children are not growing properly; 1 child in 260 falls below 0.4th **centile** and 50% of these will have growth problems; 16% of infants and children admitted to hospital are underweight, 15% have **stunted growth** and 8% are **wasted**.

In addition, 84% of children under 4 years old have an inadequate iron intake, with toddlers from socially deprived and ethnic minority groups being particularly affected. However, of these only a minority is referred for nutritional assessment. For further information on child nutrition, see http://www.bapen.org.uk.

There have been several reports in recent years highlighting the poor nutritional state of the elderly in hospitals and care homes. The Age Concern report (2006), 'Hungry to be Heard', can be accessed at www.ageconcern.org.uk.

'... six out of ten older people are at risk of becoming malnourished, or their situation getting worse, in hospital. Malnourished patients stay in hospital for longer, are three times as likely to develop complications during surgery, and have a higher mortality rate than well-fed patients.'

The European Nutrition for Health Alliance produced a report in 2005 entitled 'Malnutrition Within an Ageing Population: A Call for Action', the objective of which was 'To raise awareness of the urgent need to prevent malnutrition and ensure that effective nutritional support is available to all those affected across all community and clinical settings.' See www.fhf.org.uk/.

Loss

...nething about it? Are you encouraged to make suggestions?

centile
a method of comparing the weight and height of children to others of the same age, e.g. 0.4th centile – 99.6% of children of the same age will be heavier/ taller than a child on this centile

stunted growth
the child's increase in height has been slowed down

wasted
muscle has been lost

of function

Inability to prepare food
- Poor dental health
- Difficulty using food containers
- Difficulty reading food labels

Poverty

- Cannot afford to get to sources of good, cheap food
- Cannot afford good-quality food

'Why does malnutrition occur?'

Mobility

- Poor mobility
- Disability
- Poor transport links
- Difficulty accessing local shops

Psychological factors

- Isolation and loneliness
- Confusion
- Depression
- Anxiety
- Bereavement

Source: European Nutrition for Health Alliance 2005

Some of the problems that lead to malnutrition among service users

Nutritional screening tools

nutritional screening tool

an aid to identify service users at risk of malnutrition

A number of tools have been developed for conducting **nutritional screening**. Of these the Malnutrition Universal Screening Tool (MUST) was developed by the Malnutrition Advisory Group to screen adults for malnutrition, even if weight and/or height cannot be measured. It can be used to assess those who are obese as well as underweight. Any member of staff responsible for nutritional screening should undertake training. Do not carry out nutritional screening unless you have completed the training.

body mass index (BMI)

weight in kg divided by height in metres squared. It is used as an indicator of nutritional status

Screening provides a way of identifying those at risk of undernutrition. Using the MUST, it looks at **body mass index** (BMI), recent change in weight, the length of time it has taken to unintentionally lose/gain weight, and the presence of an illness resulting in no dietary intake for more than five days (or likely to result in no dietary intake for more than five days). It also considers the likelihood of poor dietary intake. ('Nutrition support in Adults', NICE, 2006)

The tool groups service users into low, medium, or high risk of malnutrition and also identifies the obese. It provides guidance on how to interpret the findings, and suggests appropriate care plans. For more information on the use of the nutritional screening tool, see http://www.bapen.org.uk.

Community care workers and managers of sheltered housing schemes frequently see elderly people. These workers are in an ideal position to refer people for nutritional screening, so that undernutrition can be recognised quickly. It might be assumed that people delivering meals could be helpful here, however, they are often volunteers and their visits only last for a minute or two, so they are unlikely to be in a position to contribute in this way.

Signs such as clothing that is too big, loose rings and poorly fitting dentures are obvious indicators that someone has lost a lot of weight. Conversely tight clothing and rings indicate that weight has been gained.

Care planning

The responsibility for care planning lies with health and social care staff qualified to Level 4. This could be a qualified nurse or someone with, or working towards, NVQ Level 4, although NVQ Level 3 qualified staff often contribute towards the care-planning process. The nutritional **care plan** will detail the best ways to maximise an individual's dietary intake and it is the responsibility of all care workers to ensure that these measures are carried out.

The care-planning process should include discussion with the service user about their own understanding of their dietary needs. Personal preferences should be included wherever possible. The care plan should document any special diet needed, including allergies and religious and medical constraints. If someone has a condition such as dementia, that prevents them from expressing needs and preferences, you should ask relatives about any likes and dislikes, so that care workers can serve foods that the person will enjoy and that meet any medical needs. You should also note if the service user needs any assistance or aids to allow them to manage their meals independently. Any instructions about consistency of food should also be documented. The state of the service user's mouth and teeth and details of their dentist should also be noted. Once the needs assessment has been completed, the next stage is to plan how the needs will be met, and carry out the care according to the plan. For example, if it is noticed that dentures do not fit, the dentist should be called in to arrange for new dentures to be provided.

care plan

a required document that sets out in detail the way daily care and support must be provided to an individual. It may also be known as an 'individual plan'; ' plan of support', etc.

Activity 12

Here is an example of a care plan to record an assessment of nutritional needs on admission, and a record of eating and drinking patterns during a hospital stay.

Nutritional needs assessment

Weight on admission:

Recent weight gain or loss?   Yes ☐   No ☐

If 'yes', please give details:

Appetite on admission: Good ☐   Satisfactory ☐   Poor ☐

Usual appetite: Good ☐   Satisfactory ☐   Poor ☐

Special diet required?   Yes ☐   No ☐

If 'yes', please give details:

Dentition: adequate/inadequate *

False teeth: Full set/part set/top set/bottom set/loose *

Able to feed independently/with encouragement/needs assistance *

Preparation of meals before admission: Independent/light meals only/meals on wheels/all meals provided *

Other factors: Visually impaired/confused *

* delete as necessary

Date									
Shift	**E**	**L**	**N**	**E**	**L**	**N**	**E**	**L**	**N**
Eating full meal									
part meal									
with encouragement									
with assistance									
supplement taken									
declines to eat +									
Drinking independently									
with encouragement									
with assistance									
declines to drink +									
nil orally & mouth care									

+ Make note in daily record the reason for refusal.

Look at the care plans at your place of work. Do they capture all the information needed to identify malnutrition on admission, people at risk of malnutrition, or to quickly notice if a service user is eating or drinking sufficient amounts?

Risk assessment

Risks associated with eating and drinking include **undernutrition**, **overnutrition**, food poisoning, dehydration, allergic reaction, choking, or scalding.

All staff involved with planning, producing, and serving of meals and beverages must be aware of service users identified as 'at risk' of any of the above, so that appropriate choices are offered, assistance is available, and that intake of food and fluid is monitored.

Oral health

A major cause of refusal to eat is poor oral health. Mouth pain can be caused by poorly fitting dentures, tooth decay, loose teeth, mouth ulcers, sore tongue, oral thrush, and oral cancer. You should pass on any concerns you have about the mouth of a service user. Many problems can be easily rectified by a dentist, or with simple medication from the GP. By reporting any concerns you can make eating a pleasure again for a service user.

More than half of elderly people still have some, if not all, of their own teeth, and should be encouraged to brush their teeth regularly to prevent sore gums and tooth decay, as well as to freshen the mouth before and after eating.

Mouth care is the key to preventing a sore mouth. Even if a person has a full set of dentures they should still clean the mouth with a toothbrush and toothpaste twice a day. Using a soft bristled brush, the gums, the tongue and roof of the mouth should be cleaned to remove plaque.

You should also make sure that dentures are cleaned thoroughly with toothpaste to remove any food debris before being soaked in denture cleaner. Make sure you brush all the surfaces of the dentures, including the surface that comes into contact with the gums and the roof of the mouth. If fixative is used, make sure you remove it all each day so it doesn't build up, which would cause soreness. Brush the dentures again after soaking.

1. How does the person-centred approach affect the provision of food and drink?
2. What factors are assessed when screening adults for malnutrition?
3. What information about diet should be included on a service user's care plan?

undernutrition

a deficiency of calories or of one or more essential nutrients

overnutrition

a condition that results from eating too much, eating too many of the wrong things, not taking enough exercise, or taking too many vitamins or other dietary replacements

Stephanie has just come on shift after a week's holiday. Lunch has just finished and she notices that Maria hasn't eaten any of hers. As she is scraping the plate into the waste bin, Stephanie casually says to the senior, Paul, 'I see Maria's still not eating.' Paul looks concerned, 'What do you mean?' he asks. 'Well, when I was looking after her before I went on holiday she didn't eat anything for two days,' says Stephanie.

This highlights the importance of reporting concerns about service users, as a doctor should have seen Maria several days ago.

If service users are confused it is even more important to record information such as dietary intake, as they are unlikely to report a problem themselves.

In this section you will learn your role, and the limits of your role, in keeping a check on the service user's condition and the treatments aimed at ensuring they receive adequate nutrition.

What you need to learn

- Documentation and record-keeping.
- Observing and reporting concerns.
- Seeking advice and guidance.
- Education of individuals and their significant others.

Documentation and record-keeping

To make sure that all service users receive adequate nutrition and are offered foods that are acceptable to them, any information about special diets and preferences should be documented, usually in the care plan. A senior care worker, qualified to NVQ Level 4, should prepare the care plan, or it can be done by a carer working towards Level 4, with their assessor or mentor providing supervision. All staff dealing with service users should contribute to the care plan where relevant (see Section 2.1, page 57).

Recording whether or not someone has eaten his or her meals can also be very useful. It is easy to miss recording that a service user has refused to eat or left several meals in succession. Because of shift patterns they could have been cared for by several different people, with each one thinking that refusing to eat or leaving a meal was a one-off occurrence.

If someone refuses a meal, this should be recorded, as should evidence of strategies used to coax the person to eat. This should include a comment that you asked why the food was being refused. In order to try to encourage the person to take their meal you might:

- substitute food offered for something else, such as a supplement drink or a glass of milk
- cut food up
- provide adapted cutlery or crockery
- offer to help the person eat
- offer food again later, perhaps when pain relief has taken effect, for example.

In the event of an enquiry into the care a service user has received, clear documentation can prove that you, as a carer, did everything you could to ensure that food was taken.

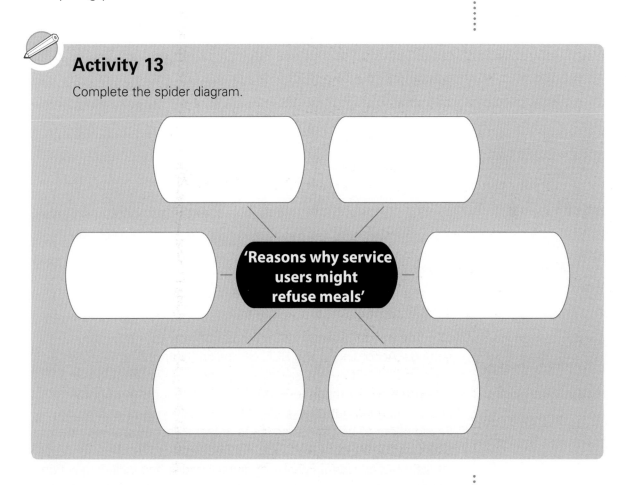

Activity 13

Complete the spider diagram.

'Reasons why service users might refuse meals'

Recording changes in weight is also very important in the case of some service users, particularly those with heart failure and kidney failure, who may retain fluid in the body, which can cause problems such as breathing difficulties if the fluid collects around the lungs. If a service user is being weighed daily, an increase in body weight of 1kg for three consecutive days indicates that they are retaining fluid, which could indicate the need for medical intervention, for example the person may need to take a diuretic (water) tablet. You should therefore bring this to the attention of the person in charge, who can decide what needs to be done. Other signs of fluid retention include breathlessness and swollen feet and ankles.

FLUID CHART (ADULT)

PLEASE SEE REVERSE FOR NOTES ON USE OF THIS CHART

ORAL INTAKE				INTRAVENOUS THERAPY * Before starting this section remember to enter TIME and name of I.V. fluid already in progress and amount brought forward from the previous chart							OUTPUT							
TIME	FLUID	ml	ORAL TOTAL SO FAR ml	STARTED		ENDED		* BROUGHT FORWARD ml		TIME	URINE ml	URINE TOTAL SO FAR ml	ASPIRATE OR VOMIT ml	ASP/VOM TOTAL SO FAR ml	DRAIN ml	DRAIN ml	COMMENTS
				TIME	FLUID	TIME	ml	COMMENTS									
12.00	TEA	250	250	09.00	HARTMANS	12.00	1000	IV DISCONTINUED		12.30	300	300	NIL	NIL	–	–	
13.00	WATER	250	500							16.00	500	800	100	100			
13.45	TEA	250	750							18.30	600	1200		100			

TIME	TOTAL – ORAL	ml	TOTAL – I.V.	ml	CARRIED FORWARD ml	TOTALS	URINE ml	ASPIRATE/VOMIT ml	DRAIN ml	DRAIN ml

SURNAME ADAMS	OTHER NAMES JULIE	UNIT NUMBER 60677-241	WARD 2A	DATE 28/06/07	CODE CRC 017

An example of a fluid balance chart

Documentation of dietary intake is not carried out in all care settings. According to the RCN campaign 'Nutrition Now', 'Over a quarter (28%) of nurses said there is not a requirement in the nursing documentation for them to record patients' nutritional needs.' As good nutrition is essential to recovery and well-being it would seem to be good practice to at least discuss diet with service users on admission. Clearly it is not necessary to record everyone's intake, but early identification of dietary needs and including action points in the care plan are effective ways of reducing the incidence of malnutrition in hospitals and care settings. You can access the RCN campaign at http://www.rcn.org.uk.

Observing and reporting concerns

As well as recording that someone has refused to eat the meal offered, or has eaten very little, you should report this to the person in charge. Sometimes refusal of a meal may indicate a problem that needs to be dealt with quickly. Abdominal pain (stomach ache) could indicate a serious problem, such as appendicitis, severe constipation, or a bowel obstruction, so don't assume it is just indigestion. Slow eaters may be experiencing pain from poorly fitting dentures, which could easily be remedied. If someone has communication problems they may not be able to tell you that they do not like the food that has been offered. Slow eating or pushing away the food could indicate this, so your skills of observation are important for identifying that a problem exists. Even if you are not able to work out what the problem is, always report your observations to a more experienced member of staff.

You should report immediately if you notice someone having difficulty breathing during a meal, which could indicate choking or an allergic reaction to food. Allergic reactions can also cause a rash, so this should be reported, even if breathing problems have not developed, as the next time the person comes into contact with the same food the reaction could be much more severe.

Breathing problems, such those caused by asthma, heart disease or a chest infection can also affect a person's ability to eat properly, and these difficulties should be reported. Changing the medication regime could provide relief. Offering foods that are easier to chew and swallow might also help in a person who is exhausted from struggling to breathe.

Seeking advice and guidance

As you are still receiving training, you would not be expected to solve all the problems you encounter when providing food and drink to your service users. Always seek advice from more experienced staff if you are unsure about how to deal with a situation. Sometimes the dietary problems are beyond the experience of any of the staff in a care setting, and in such cases advice and guidance must be sought from specialists, such as a dietician, who can prescribe a special diet. Chewing and swallowing problems can sometimes be improved with exercises recommended by a speech therapist, so an assessment should be requested. If a service user is not eating properly because they are feeling sick, a doctor can prescribe anti-emetics to reduce nausea. An occupational therapist can supply eating aids. The role of these specialists is covered in more detail in Section 2.4, pages 78–83.

Educating individuals and their significant others

1. Why is it important to keep accurate records about dietary intake and the efforts that have been made to ensure that service users have an adequate diet?

2. What might you notice at mealtimes that would make you concerned enough to report your concerns to a senior member of staff?

3. What are the limits of your role in monitoring the condition of service users?

Anyone who needs a special diet and who is responsible for preparing their own meals will need detailed information about the foods that they can or cannot eat. Someone who is unable to chew or swallow properly will need to know the methods of preparing appropriate foods. Similarly, **significant others**, such as those caring for such people, should receive education on how to prepare special meals.

Dieticians will supply a list of suitable foods to choose from as well as those that should be avoided. This will enable the service user to enjoy a varied diet within the constraints of their condition.

There are several voluntary organisations for people with specific conditions requiring dietary advice. For some conditions the diet simply requires the avoidance of foods containing specific substances, such as gluten or lactose, and a list of foods that are free of these substances may be all that is needed (see page 24). For others the diet can be more complicated. For example, a diet aimed at reducing weight needs to consider calorie intake, as well as ensuring that all the vital nutrients are included. Educating people to consult the labels on food packaging can help them to develop confidence in their ability to choose suitable foods. It is not the role of the care worker to create a special diet, but you should be able to follow the recommendations of the dietician.

significant others
the family, friends and advocates of the individual receiving care and support

Activity 14

A lot of useful information and advice is available on the Internet, and from leaflets produced by organisations to support people who require a special diet. You can access the advice on diabetes, coeliac disease and cancer at www.diabetes.org.uk, www.coeliac.co.uk, http://www.cancerhelp.org.uk.

If you do not have access to the Internet, information is available from the addresses below, or you may find leaflets at your GP's surgery or local library.

Diabetes UK
Macleod House
10 Parkway
London NW1 7AA
Tel 020 7424 1000
Fax 020 7424 1001

Coeliac UK
Suites A–D Octagon Court
High Wycombe
Bucks HP11 2HS
Tel 01494 437 278
Fax 01494 474 349

Cancer Research UK
61 Lincoln's Inn Fields
London WC2A 3PX
Tel 020 7061 8355
Freephone 0800 226237

2.3 Understand the role, responsibilities and boundaries of the worker in relation to food handling and serving

In this section you will learn your role, and the limits of your role, in ensuring that food is prepared and handled properly.

What you need to learn

- Personal hygiene.
- Food hygiene.
- Promoting independence.
- Support at mealtimes.

Personal hygiene

As a care worker, you have a responsibility to do everything you can to ensure that you do not put your service users at risk. One area that you should take very seriously is your personal hygiene when serving food. Effective handwashing has been identified as one of the best ways to prevent infection spreading.

Hands should be washed frequently throughout the food preparation and cooking process, particularly before touching food, after touching raw meat, poultry, fish and eggs, after visiting the toilet, after touching the waste bin or animals, and before touching surfaces such as cupboard, fridge and kettle handles.

Effective handwashing only takes about 20 seconds with practice, but you should be more concerned about thoroughness than speed. Use the diagram below to practise your technique.

1. Wet hands with running water.

2. Rub hands together with soap and lather well, covering all surfaces.

3. Weave fingers and thumbs together and slide them back and forth.

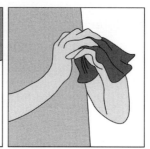

4. Rinse hands under a stream of clean, running water until all soap is gone.

5. Blot hands dry with clean towel.

It is also important to wear a clean apron when serving meals to protect food from contamination from your work clothes. Take particular care to wash your hands thoroughly after helping an individual to use the toilet or bedpan.

If you have been dealing with a service user who has had diarrhoea or has been vomiting you should be especially careful about your personal hygiene, and if possible avoid dealing with food at all. If you have had this type of infection yourself you should not go near food being prepared for others until you have been free of symptoms for 48 hours.

You should wear a clean uniform every day and bring a spare one with you in case your uniform gets contaminated with anything that could pose a risk of infection.

Staff should tie their hair back or wear a hairnet or close-fitting hat when preparing food, as this will reduce the risk of hair falling into food, or staff touching their hair during food preparation.

You should not wear a watch or jewellery when preparing food, as these are places where bacteria may get trapped.

You should not eat or touch your face near your mouth or nose whilst you are preparing food, as germs from your mouth or nose could be transferred to the food you are preparing.

Activity 15

Contact your local environmental health officer (EHO) and ask if he or she would visit your workplace to show the staff correct handwashing techniques. Since part of their role is education, EHOs are usually pleased to be invited into workplaces to demonstrate how to correctly follow hygiene procedures, given that the aim of the service is to encourage good practice, not issue sanctions.

Food hygiene

It is everyone's role to practise good food hygiene. A food hygiene certificate is an essential qualification for those involved in food preparation in the care sector. Many care settings encourage staff to complete a Chartered Institute of Environmental Health Level 2 Award in Food Safety qualification or that of the Royal Society for the Promotion of Health. Anyone wishing to deliver food-handling training should attend additional training to equip them with the skills to teach others about food hygiene.

Food hygiene is vital to ensure that food is stored, prepared and cooked in a way that will prevent food-borne infection. It is also practised to ensure that such infections are not spread between individuals. For any service users, and particularly those with reduced immunity, food poisoning can lead to severe illness and can be fatal. It is your responsibility as a care worker to make sure you understand good practice in food hygiene and to carry this out whenever you are dealing with food.

In handling food, as a general rule:

- wash hands frequently, especially after using the toilet or helping others with the toilet or bedpan
- do not prepare food if you have had a stomach bug
- raw and **ready-to-eat** foods must be kept separate from one another
- keep poisonous substances, such as cleaning materials, away from food preparation areas
- keep food covered
- make sure pests cannot get into food
- clean and clear up as you go along
- use a clean cloth every day for wiping surfaces
- replace any broken cooking utensils
- chill food quickly, but do not put warm food into the refrigerator

ready-to-eat

food that is cooked or raw and will not be cooked again before eating

- defrost frozen food thoroughly
- cook and reheat food thoroughly
- observe **use-by dates**
- ensure fridge and freezer are at the correct temperature.

use-by date

food eaten after this date could cause food poisoning

Storage of food

It is important to store foods correctly to ensure that it is not going to cause food poisoning. The table below is a guide to storing food to ensure it is fit to eat.

Food type	Storage place	Temperature	Length of time
Raw meat, poultry and fish	Bottom shelf of fridge or freeze	Between 1°C and 4°C	Cook by use-by date
Pre-packed cooked meat, poultry and fish	Fridge above any raw meat, or freeze	Between 1°C and 4°C	Once opened eat within two days
Dairy produce	Fridge above any raw meat	Between 1°C and 4°C	Do not exceed use-by date
Ready-to-eat food	Fridge above any raw meat	Between 1°C and 4°C	Do not exceed use-by date
Dried and tinned foods (before opening)	Food cupboard or larder	Room temperature	Do not exceed use-by date
Tinned food (after opening)	Fridge, transfer to another container	Between 1°C and 4°C	Once opened, eat within two days
Vegetables	Dark cupboard, or vegetable rack	Room temperature	Eat when as fresh as possible as vitamins decrease as vegetables age
Fruit	Fruit bowl	Room temperature	Eat when as fresh as possible as vitamins decrease as fruit ages
Frozen foods	Freezer	Below −18°C	Taste deteriorates after 'best-before' date

contaminate

transmit germs from one food to another

Food can become a health hazard in various ways. Being aware of the ways bacteria (germs) can breed and spread from one food to another will enable you to avoid situations where you accidentally **contaminate** food. Contaminated food can cause food poisoning, which can be fatal in vulnerable service users such as the elderly, the chronically sick and the very young.

Some foods pose a high risk of causing food poisoning, especially eggs, meat and poultry. Raw eggs, meat and poultry should always be treated as contaminated, and you must wash your hands thoroughly after touching any of these. You must never let raw foods touch any other food that is not going to be cooked before it is eaten. Cooking will kill germs, however cooked meats should be eaten straight away or covered and put into the refrigerator, as if they are left out they will soon attract more bacteria, which will quickly start to multiply.

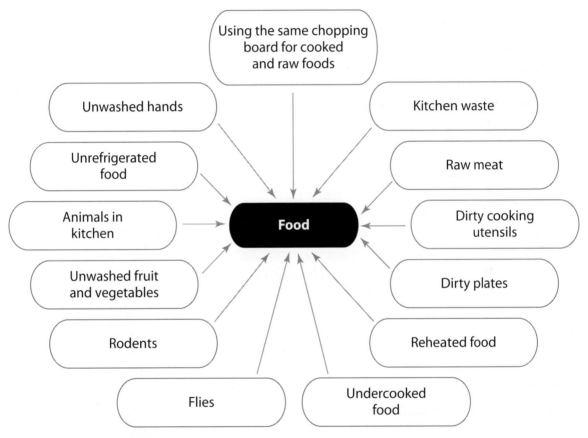

The sources of food contamination

At room temperature bacteria double in number approximately every 20 minutes. So after 24 hours 1 bacterium could have multiplied to 470,000,000,000,000,000,000!

Activity 16

Look at the diagram on page 69, and write below some basic rules to prevent food becoming contaminated by germs.

_____

_____

_____

_____

_____

_____

_____

_____

_____

_____

Preparation of food

Food poisoning is often caused when harmful bacteria on one food are spread by hand, kitchen utensils or direct contact to cross-contaminate other foods. A strict routine should be adopted to prevent contamination of food during preparation. Care must be taken to prevent raw meat, fish or eggs touching ready-to-eat food. Raw meat should be stored at the bottom of the fridge, as any blood that drips from it is likely to contain bacteria and could contaminate any food below, causing food poisoning if it contaminates foods that will be served without further cooking. Check frequently to ensure that out-of-date food is not left in the refrigerator, where it may contaminate other foods.

There should be different chopping boards and knives for different types of food: bread, dairy, raw meat, cooked meat and vegetables. Surfaces should be scrupulously clean, with no crevices where bacteria could breed. Work surfaces and the inside of the fridge should be regularly cleaned with anti-bacterial spray. Cloths must be washed and replaced with clean ones every day.

Activity 17

Go into your kitchen at work and look at the colour coding for chopping boards. Write down which boards should be used for which foods.

People's own home kitchens

If you work in the community, you may be preparing food in a service user's kitchen. Most service users' kitchens will be clean and in good condition, however, some facilities may be poor. You need to work around this, as it is your responsibility to ensure that the service user is not put at risk of food poisoning or contamination. You should always recommend fresh food wherever possible, but it may be that storage facilities are so poor that the person will receive a more nutritious meal by using convenience food that you know is in a fit state, rather than food that has deteriorated. You may also need to give advice about storage of dry foods. Packets should be stored off the floor and preferably on a shelf or in a cupboard that is dry and inaccessible to **vermin**. Signs of mice and rats include droppings, gnawed holes in packets, and smear marks on skirting boards. If you see signs of vermin you should contact the local authority environmental health department for advice.

vermin

pests such as rats, mice, flies and cockroaches, which carry germs that could cause food poisoning

It is the responsibility of the care worker to make sure that the conditions of the cooking facilities do not put service users at risk of being contaminated

Cooking food

Frozen meat and poultry must be thoroughly thawed before they are cooked.

Use different utensils for raw meat, cooked meat, poultry and fish, and keep raw and cooked food separate, otherwise bacteria can be passed from the raw food to the cooked food.

Raw meat, poultry and fish must be cooked for the correct amount of time, according to their weight, and at the correct temperature to ensure all bacteria are killed. Encourage service users to use a cookery book, or create a simple chart of cooking temperatures and times. Always preheat the oven before putting food in and turn meat over part way through cooking. All meats and raw eggs can cause *Salmonella* food poisoning, but you should take particular care with poultry and pork. Check that chicken is cooked by testing with a skewer or a fork. The juices should run clear and the meat should be white. Cooked fish has a different appearance from raw fish; raw fish has a translucent appearance whereas cooked fish is opaque and flakes easily. Beef and lamb can be served undercooked, although some people do not like to see blood running from meat, so enquire about personal preferences.

Stir sauces and soups during cooking to ensure that they are hot right through.

Eggs should be cooked until the yolk is firm. Never be tempted to make foods with raw eggs, or taste uncooked cake mix with raw egg in it.

Rice can cause food poisoning. Rice grains can contain spores of harmful bacteria, which may not be killed during cooking. It is alright to eat the rice immediately after cooking, but if you leave it at room temperature, the bacteria may multiply, and are not killed even by reheating. Therefore, if you want to eat cooked rice later it must be quickly cooled down and put in the refrigerator, which should be set below 5°C. Spores will not harm you unless they start to germinate. See http://www.keepingfoodsafe/ asksamcooking/

Pulses, such as red kidney beans, pose another risk if not cooked properly. If you use dried beans and pulses they must be soaked before cooking, and cooked according to the instructions or they may be poisonous. Tinned beans and tinned pulses can be used without soaking, so these are a safer option to use with service users.

It is good practice to check food with a food thermometer to ensure it has reached the required temperature. Pork and poultry should reach 90°C, lamb 80°C, and beef 75°C for 'well done', 70°C for 'medium' and 60°C for 'rare'.

The Food Standards Agency document 'Safe Food, Better Business' states that hot-held food should be kept at 63°C or above to prevent bacteria from reproducing. However, hot-holding will reduce the nutritional value of food, so should be avoided if possible. Many organisations require staff to document that food temperatures have been checked in case there are any incidents that could point to poor food hygiene. You can buy talking food thermometers for people who are visually impaired.

Once food is cooked it should either be served immediately or quickly cooled and then refrigerated for use later.

Food poisoning

Food poisoning is caused when food contaminated with bacteria, or the toxins they produce, is consumed. The most common causes of food poisoning are *Campylobacter* and *Salmonella*. Less common causes are *E coli*, *Clostridium*, particularly *Clostridium difficile* and *Listeria monocytogenes*.

Campylobacter

This is the most common cause of food poisoning. There were nearly 63,000 cases of *Campylobacter* in the UK in 2000. The symptoms include diarrhoea (which may be bloody), vomiting, stomach cramps, and high temperature. Symptoms can last up to a week. *Campylobacter* is found in most raw poultry and is common in raw meat. Like *Salmonella*, it

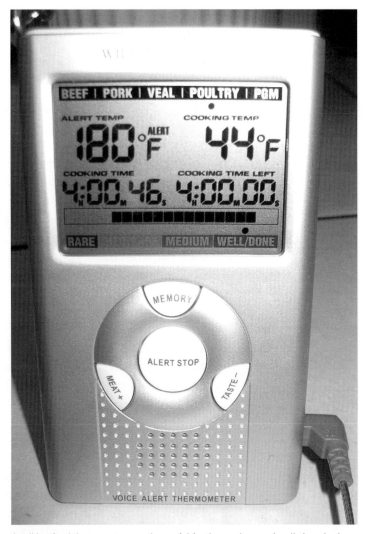

A talking food thermometer may be useful for those who are visually impaired

can also be contracted by drinking unpasteurised milk. This can lead to dehydration and even death.

Salmonella

Nearly 17,000 people caught *Salmonella* in 2000. Symptoms are similar to *Campylobacter*. Although most people recover without treatment, there is a risk that a person can become dehydrated, which can be extremely dangerous, and in some cases can be fatal. Children, elderly people and those with low immunity are particularly at risk.

Salmonella is most commonly found in raw meat, unpasteurised milk, eggs and poultry, but has occasionally been found in vegetables such as beansprouts.

Food that is contaminated with *Campylobacter* or *Salmonella* will look, smell and taste normal, so correct handling and cooking are very important.

E coli

Most *E coli* bacteria are harmless to humans as they live naturally in the gut, however there were 1,147 cases of the strain *E coli* 0157 in the UK in 2000. *E coli* 0157 can cause diarrhoea which may contain blood, and like any other form of food poisoning can, in severe cases, lead to kidney failure and anaemia. Up to 5% of people affected by *E coli* die from this condition. It is caught from eating inadequately cooked meat, but some cases have been traced to other foods that have been contaminated through poor food hygiene. Cases have also been transmitted from person to person through poor hygiene practices when caring for affected individuals.

Clostridium perfringens

Clostridium is found in the gut of humans and animals. Symptoms include stomach ache, diarrhoea and sometimes nausea. It is found in raw meat and poultry. There were 166 cases in 2000, so it is not common, but it can be fatal in the elderly and people who are already ill.

Clostridium difficile

Whilst *Clostridium difficile* is not a food-borne illness as such, it can be spread through poor food-hygiene practice and is very common in health-dare settings. It is occasionally found in the gut of adults, but is commonly found in the gut of infants, even though it is usually symptomless, so those working with babies need to be particularly aware of this infection. An adult who has *Clostridium difficile* will have diarrhoea and will pass a large amount of spores in the faeces, which can contaminate surfaces in the surrounding environment. If care staff and service users fail to wash their hands thoroughly before preparing or eating food, bacteria can be ingested (taken into the body with food), causing infection to occur.

Listeriosis

Listeriosis, the condition caused by infection with *Listeria monocytogenes*, is not common, only causing 113 cases in 2000. However, it is increasing year on year. It may go unnoticed, or cause mild flu-like symptoms with or without diarrhoea and vomiting, but it is particularly dangerous in the second and third trimesters of pregnancy as it can cause miscarriage, still birth, premature birth and infections in the newborn, such as eye infections, pneumonia, or meningitis. *Listeria* can be found in chilled meals, soft cheeses, pâtés and smoked fish. Pregnant women are advised to avoid these foods.

People with weakened immune systems, such as those with cancer, are more vulnerable to listeriosis, and it can be fatal in those with HIV and AIDS.

Promoting independence

As a care worker it is your responsibility to encourage service users to maintain their independence and keep control over their lives where possible. For example, service users can be encouraged to plan their own menu, make a shopping list, and buy and cook their own food. It can be very rewarding to work in this way and enable people to retain a degree of independence and maintain dignity. Service users with learning disabilities and mental ill-health often need guidance, but can easily manage to provide meals for themselves with support and encouragement.

As a care worker, it is your job to support people to do things for themselves, not to do everything for them

CORNWALL COLLEGE
LEARNING CENTRE

They may also need encouraging to practise good kitchen hygiene. You should not be tempted to take over and do tasks for people who are capable of some degree of independence.

A report entitled 'Home Life, Quality of Life in Care Homes' was published by Help the Aged in November 2006. In it, a service user described how living in a residential care setting may 'make you lazy', since the staff do everything for the residents. It is easy for care wokers to forget that many service users would like to be active, and might welcome the chance to do some of their own cooking or laundry.

The National Minimum Standards for Care Homes for Older People acknowledge that many older people still want to retain some capacity to play an active part in preparing some food or drink for themselves. Health and safety restrictions may mean that it is dangerous to allow residents into the main kitchen, but care providers should look at alternative ways of allowing service users to be involved in cooking for themselves, for example, by organising cooking activities or providing a kitchenette for them to use.

The National Minimum Standards for Care Homes for Adults Aged 18 to 65 years require service users to be actively supported to help plan, prepare and serve meals.

Activity 18

Ask your supervisor if they would mind you working with a service user to do some cooking. If they agree, ask a service user if they would like to cook. Try to get them to be as independent as possible, including choosing what to cook, doing the shopping, weighing and measuring, washing up afterwards. It can be hard to stop yourself interfering!

Support at mealtimes

If a service user is having difficulty eating unaided, it is your role as a care worker to assist them. This could be by providing suitable cutlery or crockery, or cutting up food, to enable them to manage independently. The advantage of this is that the person can eat at a pace that suits them, and is not waiting for someone to help them.

It also encourages independence and maintains their dignity.

Some people really cannot manage to eat independently, and as a carer you need to recognise when to intervene. For example, if the person is eating so slowly that his or her food has gone cold, and everyone else has finished eating, then the benefits of maintaining independence may be less than the potential feelings of embarrassment at taking so long. Also, the person would probably be eating alone for the latter part of the meal. However, some people may prefer not to be helped, so you must take their wishes into account when planning care, and you should never take over without the service user's agreement.

You may also assist someone who cannot move their arms sufficiently or has poor muscle control, which might lead to spillages. The risk of spillages alone, however, is not reason enough to decide to help someone. The decision has to be made jointly with the service user, and their wishes taken into account.

Look back at Section 1.3, page 52, to see what is considered good practice when helping someone with their meals.

Activity 19

Write an account of an occasion when you have assisted a service user with a meal. Include information about what you did and said, and why. Remember to include reference to care values, such as dignity and maintaining independence, and explain how you achieved this.

1. Suggest five ways in which food can be contaminated and become a potential source of food poisoning.
2. Why is it important to enable service users to remain independent in providing their own meals and drinks if at all possible?
3. What is your role when working with a person who is unable to eat without help?

In this section you will learn about your role and the role of other care workers in ensuring that service users receive a nutritious diet. You need to learn who is responsible for what, so that you know how to seek advice.

What you need to learn

The role of:

- social care workers
- workers not involved in direct care
- managers
- specialist personnel.

Social care worker

The role of the social care worker in residential settings involves assisting with ordering, giving out meals, ensuring that the service users have everything to hand they need, such as drinks, and ensuring they know the meal has arrived. Before leaving service users to eat their meals, make sure they can manage. Anyone who needs assistance should have a care worker available as soon as the meal arrives. You should keep a close eye on anyone who is likely to have difficulties during the meal, for example anyone who is at risk of choking or spilling their food or drink. It is also the role of the social care worker to report any refusal to eat or drink to a senior member of staff.

In community settings the social care worker is responsible for ensuring that service users have sufficient food in their home to meet their dietary needs. How this is done varies from person to person. If the service user is mentally competent, it is not for the care worker to comment on the food the individual wishes to eat. However if a service user asks for advice on diet, or comments on a problem such as constipation, the care worker could report back to the community care manager that the service user needs a visit to discuss ways to improve their nutrition.

If you are a community care assistant and the only person who regularly visits an individual, you are responsible for noticing if a service user needs more help. You may, for example, notice that food is not being thrown away, and stale or out-of-date food is in the fridge. You should discuss with the service user if they need more help, and could report back to the community care manager that a further assessment is necessary. All service users should be periodically reviewed anyway, as needs change over time as individuals become more or less fit.

Workers not involved in direct care

Cook

The cook is responsible for planning and providing a choice of nutritious food and catering for individuals with special diets. Whilst the cook does not legally need any qualification other than a food hygiene certificate, he or she should have a good understanding of nutrition, and should know how to prepare foods of different consistencies. Unqualified catering staff are unlikely to be able to meet the nutritional needs of the service users.

The cook must have a thorough understanding of constituents of foods, so that they know which foods to avoid when preparing special diets and how to construct a balanced diet whilst maintaining nutritional content through the most appropriate cooking methods.

The cook is responsible for the food hygiene practices, and may also take responsibility for ordering food for the setting.

Kitchen assistant

The kitchen assistant's role in relation to nutrition and well-being is to assist the cook in the preparation, cooking and serving of meals and to clean catering equipment and surfaces in the kitchen and dining room. He or she may also be responsible for ensuring the correct storage of all dry and perishable goods, as soon as possible after delivery to reduce the risk of food poisoning.

Administrator

The administrator is not significantly involved in the provision of food and drink. The role is limited to tasks such as providing menus; however some administrators will assist service users in choosing from the menu.

Ancillary worker

It is the ancillary worker's role to keep the setting clean and tidy. Part of this role includes cleaning tables and crockery to ensure that no contamination occurs. Bins containing food waste need emptying daily, or when full, and should be thoroughly cleaned to prevent germs from breeding in food-preparation areas. Floors should be mopped daily, taking care to ensure that food scraps do not accumulate in corners. Carpets should be vacuumed daily to ensure that any food that has been dropped is removed, as this can attract flies and vermin.

Manager

The manager has overall responsibility for everything that happens in a care home. Sometimes this involves delegating tasks to other staff, but the manager must be confident that the member of staff is competent to carry out a delegated task. The manager must ensure that special dietary requirements are identified on admission, and that the cook is familiar with each special diet. If not, the manager should contact a dietician, through the GP, to provide education for the cook, to ensure that service users will receive the correct diet.

Similarly, other specialists, such as speech therapists, can be brought in by the manager to advise care staff about strategies to deal with swallowing and chewing difficulties. The manager must ensure that care workers are aware of special diets, allergies and other food-related problems by organising training.

The manager is responsible for resourcing the setting, for example ensuring that sufficient adapted cutlery and crockery are available. Staffing should be organised to ensure that there is always someone available to assist those who need help as soon as the meal arrives. Keeping meals hot to be served later should not be normal practice for two reasons: first, the person will not be eating his or her meal with everyone else, and secondly keeping it hot will reduce the nutritional value of the food. This therefore should only happen in unavoidable situations, such as unexpected staff shortage, or an urgent incident occurring at a mealtime.

The manager must also ensure that any medication is given before, with or after food, as necessary. They must also ensure that staff who are involved in the provision of food and drink are trained to National Minimum Standards.

Specialist personnel

Doctor

Doctors are responsible for making the initial diagnosis of conditions that require a special diet. They **refer** patients to a dietician. Some special foods can be obtained on prescription, such as gluten-free products and fortified drinks. Although most of these products can be bought, they are often very expensive. People who pay for prescriptions usually benefit from purchasing a four-monthly or an annual pre-payment certificate. Those of pensionable age (over 60 years for women; 65 years for men) do not have to pay for their prescriptions, neither do many people

refer

recommend for further assessment to another member of a health-care team with chronic illnesses. You can access information on these matters at http://www.nhpct.nhs.uk/services/prepay.html.

Doctors also prescribe medications to reduce symptoms such as nausea, inflammation of the bowel and depression, which can have a negative effect on dietary intake.

If the reason for the service user's poor diet is a mental illness they may be referred to a psychiatrist whose role would be to oversee a programme of treatment carried out by a range of health-care workers.

Dietician

Dieticians are registered with the Health Professions Council. They are specialists in the study of nutrition, whose role is to teach and advise people on eating a healthy diet, give advice and guidance about special diets and to prevent problems caused by poor nutrition. Diets prescribed by a registered dietician follow an assessment and are based on current scientific evidence and best practice. In addition, service users' individual needs and preferences are considered.

Dieticians work with people of all ages and provide expertise in the nutritional needs of a wide range of people, including those with diabetes, high blood cholesterol, gut disorders, food allergies and intolerances, mental ill-health, obesity, learning disabilities, cancer and those with swallowing difficulties. They also treat people being cared for in intensive-care units, such as patients who are unconscious, or those requiring artificial nutrition, for example PEG feeds, or supplementary nutrition.

Dieticians' work with children includes those with eating problems, such as **cleft palate**. They also work with premature babies, and with children who are not growing or putting on weight at the normal rate, as well as those who are overweight.

Dieticians also advise other health professionals, and care workers, patients and carers on how to provide a healthy diet to their service users.

> **cleft palate**
> *a condition where the roof of the mouth is not fully formed, meaning there is a hole joining the mouth and nose*

Speech and language therapist

Speech and language therapists are specialists in swallowing and chewing problems. They will assess swallowing problems and advise on the consistency of food that should be offered, and assess whether it is safe for a service user to eat and drink, or whether they should be fed by nasogastric tube or gastrostomy. For example, sometimes people choke less if their drinks are thickened. Speech and language therapists may also advise on the best position for a person to sit in when eating and drinking, and on any techniques or exercises that may improve their swallowing.

Occupational therapist

Occupational therapists specialise in providing solutions when individuals are not fully independent in their daily living activities. Eating and drinking are, of course, daily living activities.

As has already been stated, maintaining independence is very important, so an occupational therapist will assess what, precisely, is preventing an individual from being able to cook and eat independently.

As well as the adapted cutlery and crockery already described in Section 1.3, page 50, occupational therapists will suggest other aids that can enable people to prepare their own food.

A non-slip mat and a kettle tipper are two aids that help people to prepare their own food

Activity 20

Look at the photographs above. What disabilities do you think these aids would be useful for?

Try to find out about your local disability living centre; the phone number should be in your telephone directory. Try to arrange a visit to see the huge variety of aids available to help people retain their independence.

Physiotherapist

A physiotherapist may be able to help service users who have co-ordination difficulties or poor balance. The physiotherapist can advise on achieving a good sitting position.

An occupational therapist or a physiotherapist could also assess service users for mobility aids, which could enable them to continue shopping or cooking for themselves. This might include a powered wheelchair or a strong tea trolley to help carry food from the kitchen to the dining room.

Benefits adviser

If finance is affecting the quality of food being purchased, an individual may be eligible for financial help from the Department of Work and Pensions (DWP). Benefits might include Pension Credits, or Disability Living Allowance. Help with claims can be given by phoning 0800 88 22 00, or information can be obtained from http://www.direct.gov.uk/.

If you feel that any of your service users might not be claiming benefits to which they are entitled, you could obtain some information leaflets for them to look at, and supply the number above. You will need to be sensitive, as some people can take offence at any suggestion that they need financial help.

1. Which personnel might be involved in enabling a person with diabetes, who is visually impaired and uses a wheelchair following an amputation, to remain independent in catering for themselves?

2. What is the manager's role in providing food and drink in a care setting?

3 Diet and well-being

3.1 Understand what constitutes a well-balanced diet

Food provides the body with energy and nutrients to maintain good health and to be active.

The main reasons we need to eat and drink fall into four categories:

1. **Growth and repair** – tissues are constantly replaced throughout life and food is needed for this to take place. When someone is ill their nutritional needs increase.

2. **Energy** – food provides energy for physical activity. The amount needed will depend on how active a person is.

3. **Body processes** – breathing, digesting food, transmission of nerve impulses, maintaining body temperature are just a few of the processes happening in the body. Well over half of the calories we eat are used up just keeping us alive.

4. **Prevention of disease** – some foods are known to be particularly important in the prevention of certain diseases.

Poor nutrition contributes to at least 30% of coronary heart disease deaths and 25% of cancer deaths (Food Standards Agency, 2003). Eating a healthy diet can increase independence in later life, reduce the incidence of diabetes and high blood pressure, and, in pregnancy, reduce the incidence of premature and stillbirths and spina bifida. It can also help to maintain a healthy body weight. A healthy diet can also help maintain a healthy body weight. Healthy eating can be tasty and interesting, and does not have to be expensive.

Dietary advice can get extremely complicated if you try to deal with each component of food separately, however it is important to understand the different nutrients and what they are used for in the body. You should also understand the consequences of service users eating too much or too little of different food components. In this section you will learn about components of foods and deficiency diseases. At the end of the section you will learn the current advice for a healthy diet that will provide all the essential nutrients.

What you need to learn

- Water.
- Carbohydrates.
- Proteins.
- Fats.
- Minerals.
- Vitamins.

Water

Water is not only found in drinks, but is also a component of most foods, for example fresh celery is 94% water. Water makes up 70% of the body's weight. It is very important that people have an adequate intake of fluids because most of the chemical reactions that take place in the cells of the body need water. Water has several functions, including:

- regulating body temperature
- carrying nutrients around the body
- improving bowel function
- enabling chemical reactions to take place inside cells
- helping the exchange of oxygen and carbon dioxide in the lungs
- aiding the action of medicines.

water

is essential to life. It prevents dehydration, regulates body temperature and helps prevent strain on kidneys

There is medical evidence to show that water is helpful in preventing or reducing the effects of a wide variety of conditions, including:

- pressure ulcers
- constipation
- kidney stones
- heart disease
- urinary tract infections
- incontinence
- low blood pressure
- diabetes
- confusion
- skin conditions
- headaches
- blood clots.

Opinions vary about the amount of fluid an adult should drink daily, but the average recommendation is about 2 litres a day. Remember that this does not mean everyone should drink two litres of water per day, since much of a person's daily intake comes from a variety of drinks, and we also get fluid from foods such as lettuce, cucumber, soups and jelly.

Although increased intake of fluid will mean more trips to the toilet, staff time should still be reduced because there will be fewer urinary tract infections, which are a common cause of incontinence, and less soiling, which is commonly caused by constipation. Added to this is the positive effect on service users' self-esteem and dignity.

People who are admitted to hospital with a stroke or pneumonia are twice as likely to die if they are suffering from dehydration (*Nursing Standard*, September 2007).

Children and older people are particularly vulnerable to dehydration, since they sometimes don't recognise thirst, or don't ask for a drink when they need one. Older people often restrict their fluid intake, wrongly assuming that this will reduce the likelihood of incontinence.

The Royal College of Nursing and the NHS National Patient Safety Agency have developed a Hospital Hydration Best Practice Toolkit as part of the 'Nutrition Now' campaign (see page 146). It can be used in other care settings as well.

Carry out the test on page 87 to find out whether you and your colleagues need to do more to encourage service users to drink more water.

dehydration

a reduction of 1% or more of the normal water content of the body. Depending on the percentage of body weight lost, dehydration can be described as mild, moderate or severe.

Activity 21

Test your skills at keeping your service users hydrated

☐ Staff are clear about the benefits of providing more water.

☐ Staff make water available and encourage service users to drink.

☐ You have clear aims for the strategy to increase fluid intake.

☐ The whole team have been involved in the strategy.

☐ Staff decide when and where water will be provided.

☐ There is a code of conduct for providing water.

☐ Water is available throughout the day for service users and staff.

☐ Service users are actively encouraged to drink more.

☐ Service users are regularly told of the benefits of drinking more water.

☐ Service users have been asked for ideas about increasing their water consumption.

☐ Staff record whether service users drink enough.

☐ Water is available when service users are away from the setting.

☐ Extra water is available in hot weather.

☐ Service users can access toilets at all times.

☐ There is a system to ensure that clean jugs and glasses are available.

☐ There is a plan to monitor and evaluate the impact of improved water provision for service users.

☐ The toilets are well maintained and clean.

Adapted from *Nutrition Now, Toolkit* (2007)

How did you score?

Count the number of boxes you have ticked.

Score

0–5 You have made a start but more work needs to be done. To make sure that you and your service users get the health benefits of good hydration, you and/or your team should retrace your steps and look again at the areas you could not tick off. What needs to be changed to improve your score?

6–10 Well done on getting this far. With this score you will soon be on the way to establishing a successful strategy for promoting good hydration and drinking water. You can use the toolkit fact sheets and checklists to work out where you can implement change and you will soon be able to help improve your patients' hydration and well-being.

11–14 You are approaching the score for hydration best practice. With so much achieved, it is now simply a case of refining your efforts and looking at the individual areas for change.

15–17 Congratulations, you have done very well and will now be making a real difference to the health and well-being of your service users. If you did not score full marks, talk with your team about the areas you missed and how you can take the last few steps to good hydration for all.

For further information on nutrition campaigns, see www.rcn.org.uk/newsevents/campaigns/nutritionnow.

If you notice someone drinking a lot it is wise to report this to a senior member of staff, since it could indicate diabetes.

It is possible to drink too much water, although this is very unusual. One reason people sometimes drink excessive amounts of water is after using the drug ecstasy, as it increases thirst. People with impaired kidney function and some cases of heart failure are also at risk from becoming overloaded with fluids. If someone is being tube-fed, care must be taken not to overload the body with fluids. Too much fluid dilutes the blood and can affect the **electrolyte balance**.

Carbohydrates

Carbohydrates are a type of food that provides a source of energy for the body. They are the main fuel for all muscular movement. For an average person the diet should provide a large proportion of energy from carbohydrates. An active person will need a higher carbohydrate intake. Half of a person's total energy should come from carbohydrate. There are two types of carbohydrate: simple and complex. Simple carbohydrates are sugars; complex carbohydrates are starch and cellulose.

Sugars occur naturally in foods such as fruit and milk. Some of the simplest forms of sugar are glucose and fructose, found in fruit, and are easily digested by the body. Glucose can be absorbed into the bloodstream and transported around the body to provide energy. Sugars are added to many types of foods, including:

- fizzy drinks and juices
- sweets and biscuits
- jam
- cakes, pastries and puddings
- ice cream.

Sugars in food can be refined or unrefined. Refined sugar is used in cakes and biscuits; unrefined sugar is present naturally in fruit. Many foods contain sugar even though they don't taste sweet. Ketchup, beer, high-fibre snack bars and some tinned vegetables are examples and contain what are described as hidden sugars. It is recommended that not more than 11% of an adult's diet should be sugar (British Nutrition Foundation), but remember that fruit is an important part of a healthy diet.

It is recommended that about half the food we eat should be starchy foods like pasta, rice, bread, potatoes, and chapattis, with wholegrain foods being particularly healthy (Food Standards Agency). Starchy foods can be divided into simple and complex carbohydrates. Complex carbohydrates' fibre content remains

electrolyte balance

the balance of chemicals in the body

carbohydrate

a source of energy from foods such as pasta, rice, bread, potatoes intact, while many simple carbohydrates have been processed into a refined product. Simple carbohydrates are digested quickly. Although many simple carbohydrates contain refined sugars and few essential vitamins and minerals (for example honey, maple syrup and sugar), others (such as fruit, fruit juices, milk and yogurt), are packed with other essential ingredients and are a valuable part of our diet.

All starches are broken down into glucose. Any spare glucose is removed from the blood and stored as glycogen in the liver, or in fat around the body. When you need an energy boost the glycogen is converted back to glucose and goes back into the bloodstream. Starchy foods release energy more slowly than sugars, so will keep you satisfied longer.

Eating insufficient carbohydrates will result in protein being used for energy instead of for growth and repair. A diet low in carbohydrate is likely to be low in fibre (see below), vitamins A, B group, and E, calcium, magnesium, iron and potassium and **antioxidants**. (See pages 93–5 for information about vitamins and minerals.) Such a diet could increase the chances of a person developing cancer and other diseases.

If a person's diet is seriously deficient in carbohydrate, the body starts to break down fat to produce energy. This process is called ketosis. A healthy, balanced diet should provide all the glucose that is needed, so that ketosis will not take place. Ketosis may also be seen in those with anorexia nervosa. Prolonged severe ketosis can be dangerous, as it can alter the acidity of the blood, causing damage to the liver and kidneys.

Fibre is an important component of a healthy balanced diet. It comes from plant-based foods, but is not absorbed by the body. This means that fibre is not a nutrient, and contains no calories or vitamins. It is important because it helps the digestive system to process food and absorb nutrients. It lowers blood cholesterol and helps to control blood sugar levels, which in turn controls appetite.

There are two types of fibre: soluble and insoluble. Soluble fibre can be partially digested and is important in reducing cholesterol in the blood. Pulses, such as peas, beans and lentils are a good source of soluble fibre, as are oats. Insoluble fibre is contained in vegetable stalks, wholemeal cereal and brown rice, for example. It is also known as cellulose. It is important because it forms the bulk in our faeces, preventing constipation, and is thought by some experts to help prevent bowel cancer and other bowel conditions. Fibre makes people feel full, so they are less likely to overeat. For further information on fibre in the diet, see www.eatwell.gov.uk.

antioxidants

substances thought to lower the risk of developing cancer and heart disease. They also reduce the chance of oils, fats and fat-soluble vitamins from combining with oxygen and causing damage in the body, changing colour, or going rancid

fibre

an important component of a healthy balanced diet that comes from plant-based foods, e.g. vegetables and grains. Helps towards a healthy working gut

Activity 22

Look at the labels of a range of foods. The ingredient listed first is the main ingredient. See how many foods you can find which lists a sugar as the first, or one of the main ingredients.

Sometimes sugar is listed as:

- glucose or glucose syrup
- sucrose
- maltose
- dextrose
- invert sugar
- hydrolysed starch
- golden syrup
- honey
- treacle
- maple syrup
- brown sugar.

Proteins

protein

is useful for growth, repair and maintenance of the body. It is found in meat, fish, eggs, cheese, milk

amino acids

the building blocks of protein

Protein is a vital nutrient essential to health. It is used by the body for growth and repair, so it is particularly important for infants, children and adolescents, who are all growing rapidly, and for people who are ill or injured. Proteins are made up of amino acids. There are 22 different **amino acids**, which combine to form different proteins, eight of which must come from the food we eat. Animal sources of protein are meat, fish, poultry, eggs, milk and cheese. These are known as complete proteins because they provide all of the eight essential amino acids needed by humans. However, soya beans are regarded as equal to meat in protein, so are a good meat substitute in the diet of vegetarians and vegans.

Protein is used in the body in a variety of ways. All tissues in the body contain protein, including hair and bone. Enzymes and hormones are also proteins. Proteins are used in all activities taking place inside the body, such as messages travelling along nerves, digesting food, and muscles contracting.

It is unusual for people in the UK to be short of protein in their diet, and it certainly should not be the case in a residential care setting. If someone is following a vegan or vegetarian diet you must make sure it is varied, so that all the eight essential amino acids are eaten. Don't worry too much, as the body can store amino acids for a short time, so as long as the diet is varied and well balanced there shouldn't be a problem. Good vegan and vegetarian sources of protein include nuts, seeds, lentils, beans and soya. Many vegetarians eat eggs and dairy produce as well. Two ounces of kidney beans, chick peas and lentils contain as much protein as three ounces of steak. They are low in fat, and are loaded with fibre so will keep you feeling full for a long time.

Fats

It is important that we have some **fat** in our diet, as it is an important source of vitamins A, D, E and K. We also need to eat fat to make hormones, to keep our skin healthy and to prevent loss of body heat. It is high in calories, so provides energy, although current recommendations say we should get most of our energy from carbohydrates. If we eat too much fatty food it is easy to put on weight. Obesity can increase the strain on the joints, leading to mobility problems including arthritis in the knees.

There are two main types of fat: saturated and unsaturated. Most saturated fat comes from animal sources, such as lard, cream, full-fat milk, cheese, butter and the fat on meat. Saturated fat is generally solid at room temperature. Most unsaturated fat is from vegetable sources, and it is usually liquid at room temperature. Unsaturated fats contain essential fatty acids that cannot be manufactured by the body, so we need to get them from food. Unsaturated fat in the diet can lower the levels of low-density lipoproteins (LDLs), known as 'bad' cholesterol in the blood, and raise the levels of high-density lipoproteins (HDLs), known as 'good' cholesterol. HDLs protect against heart disease. Saturated fat is blamed for the high rate of heart disease and strokes in the UK. There is also some evidence that a diet high in saturated or unsaturated fat can increase the risk of cancer.

We naturally make a certain amount of cholesterol ourselves, and some people make more than others. People who naturally make a high amount of cholesterol need to be particularly careful to eat a diet that is low in saturated fat. Someone with high cholesterol can be prescribed tablets called statins, which reduce the cholesterol in the blood, thus reducing the chances of a heart attack or stroke. Some people are lucky and have a naturally low cholesterol level.

Some unsaturated fats, such as those in olives and avocados, have been found to protect against heart disease and cancer, and may reduce the severity of arthritis. These foods are often found in meals that originated in Mediterranean countries, such as Italy, Spain and Greece, where salads commonly contain olives or have an olive oil-based dressing.

The Inuit people of Alaska and Greenland also have a low incidence of heart disease despite a high-fat diet. The staple food

fats
source of energy from foods such as oil, butter, margarine

in their diet is fish that is rich in omega-3 polyunsaturated fatty acids. Research has shown that omega-3 and omega-6 fatty acids, found in fish such as salmon and mackerel, lower both cholesterol and triglyceride levels in the blood. Current advice is that we should eat oily fish twice per week. Some experts believe that fish oil can improve concentration in children with hyperactivity disorder.

The traditional Japanese diet is based around fish, rice and vegetables, and is very low in red meat, dairy products and processed foods. Consequently, the Japanese have a reputation for living to a very old age.

It is recommended that everyone, except children under 5 years of age, should have a diet low in saturated fat. Children under 5 years may struggle to get sufficient calories to meet their energy needs if their diet is low in fat. Whilst you cannot dictate to adults what they eat, it is important to offer healthy alternatives and ensure that service users are aware of healthy eating advice so they can make an informed choice.

Activity 23

Draw an arrow from each food to show whether it contains saturated fat, unsaturated fat or both. Look at the labels for information for packaged foods.

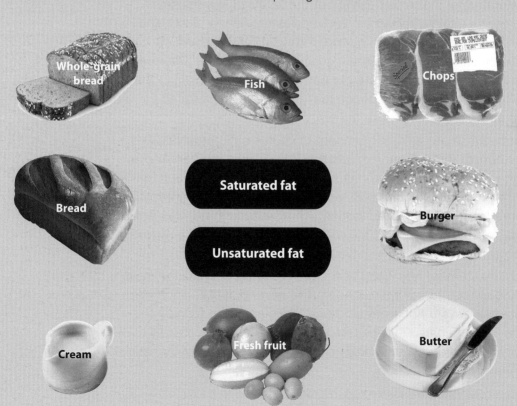

Minerals

Minerals have an important role in the healthy functioning of the body. The six major **minerals** found in food are calcium, iron, phosphorus, magnesium, sodium chloride and potassium. Even though some are only required in tiny amounts, our health suffers if we do not get what we need. They are needed for three main reasons:

- building strong bones and teeth
- controlling body fluids inside and outside cells
- turning the food we eat into energy.

Trace elements are minerals that are only required in very tiny amounts, so unless a person has a specific condition, such as a genetic abnormality, it is highly unlikely that a deficiency will occur. Trace elements include zinc, iodine, fluorine, selenium, copper, chromium, cobalt and manganese.

> **minerals**
>
> *e.g. calcium, iron, sodium, zinc – essential for maintenance of a healthy body*

Sources and functions of main minerals

Mineral	Function	Food sources	Effects of shortage	Notes
Calcium	For strong bones and teeth. Essential for blood clotting. Helps heart, muscles and nerves to work. Activates certain enzymes.	Milk, bread, flour, cheddar cheese, skimmed milk, green vegetables, sardines (with bones) and tofu.	Rickets, osteomalacia, osteoporosis (see page 12), muscle cramps.	Blood level controlled by parathyroid glands. Requires vitamin D for absorption.
Iron	Iron is needed for making the haemoglobin in red blood cells. Haemoglobin carries oxygen around the body. It is also helps the immune system and growth in childhood.	Dark green leafy vegetables, red meat, liver, apricots and dried fruit. Many breakfast cereals are fortified with iron.	Iron-deficiency anaemia causing tiredness, pale skin and brittle fingernails. Severe anaemia can cause breathlessness on exertion and can affect concentration.	Vitamin C aids absorption of iron. Iron supplements can cause constipation, nausea, vomiting and stomach ache. They also cause the faeces to be black; people should be warned of this to avoid alarm.
Phosphorus	Vital for strong bones and teeth. Involved in release of energy from food. All cells need it.	Present in nearly all foods. Good sources include wholegrain cereals, fruit, meat, eggs and milk.	Weakness, heart failure and breathing problems.	

Mineral	Function	Food sources	Effects of shortage	Notes
Magnesium	Needed for storing, burning and using energy, keeps all minerals in balance, helps muscles work properly and keeps bones and teeth strong. Important in reducing blood pressure.	Green leafy vegetables, nuts and grains.	Symptoms include insomnia, muscle cramps, palpitations, cold hands, soft or brittle nails and depression.	High levels of magnesium also causes symptoms such as nausea, muscle weakness, low blood pressure and an irregular heartbeat.
Sodium	Helps maintain fluid balance (works with potassium). Regulates blood pressure, aids muscle contraction and nerve transmission.	Occurs naturally in eggs, meat, vegetables, milk. Added to many processed foods.	Dizziness, confusion, tiredness, muscle cramps.	Salt lost by body in diarrhoea and sweating. Restriction needed in renal disease and high blood pressure.
Potassium	Helps maintain fluid balance (works with sodium). Needed for cells and nerve function. Controls pH of blood.	In most foods. Good sources include potatoes, fruit (especially bananas), vegetables and juices.	Irregular heartbeat, muscle weakness.	Most is absorbed. Excess is excreted by kidneys. Excess can cause heart failure.

Vitamins

vitamins
e.g. A, B,C,D,E – essential for maintenance of a healthy body

Vitamins are essential nutrients that your body needs in small amounts to in order to work properly. There are two types of vitamins: fat-soluble and water-soluble. Fat-soluble vitamins are found mainly in fatty foods such as vegetable oils, oily fish, butter and lard. They can be stored in the body, so we do not need to eat them daily; in fact, too much of these vitamins can be harmful. Water-soluble vitamins are found in fruit, grains and vegetables. They are destroyed by heat or exposure to the air, and cannot be stored in the body, so we need to eat foods containing these vitamins frequently. Because the body doesn't store them, these are not harmful in large quantities. Avoid soaking vegetables in water for long periods before cooking, as vitamins will be lost into the water. Do not chop vegetables too small, as the larger the surface area, the more nutrients will be lost in cooking. If you do boil vegetables, use the water to make gravy. Vitamins are also lost when food is kept hot after cooking.

neural tube defects
spina bifida and hydrocephalus, which occur during development of unborn baby

Sources and functions of vitamins

Vitamin	Function	Food sources	Effects of shortage	Water/ fat soluble	Notes
A	Helps night vision, keeps skin and linings of nose, mouth, lungs and gut healthy. **Anti-oxidant**.	Fish oil, liver, butter, cheese, eggs, milk, fruit and vegetables.	Night blindness, itching, dry and thickened skin.	Fat soluble.	Stored in liver; excess can be harmful.
B group	Release of energy from carbohydrates. Metabolism of fats and proteins, health and maintenance of nervous system.	Liver, yeast, leafy green vegetables, nuts, milk and wholegrains.	B_1 Beri-beri. B_2 Itching eyes and sore mucous membranes. B_3 Pellagra. B_6 Poor sensation in feet and confusion. B_9 (folic acid) Megaloblastic anaemia, **neural tube defects**. B_{12} Pernicious anaemia.	Water soluble.	
C	Formation of bones, teeth, and blood, wound healing, fighting infection, healthy skin and gums. Anti-oxidant.	Blackcurrants, citrus fruits, green vegetables, peppers, tomatoes.	Scurvy, poor healing, easy bruising.	Water soluble.	Not stored in body, so daily dose needed. Lost in cooking.
D	Absorption of calcium in intestine, regulates calcium and magnesium in bone tissue.	Fish liver, oily fish, eggs, milk, margarine, sunlight.	Rickets, osteomalacia, fractures.	Fat soluble.	Produced in skin by sun, stored in liver.
E	Maintains healthy muscles, anti-oxidant, protects cell membranes.	Eggs, cereal oils, vegetable oils, nuts, seeds.	Poor muscle, circulatory and nerve performance.	Fat soluble.	Stored in the body.
K	Blood clotting.	Leafy vegetables (especially spinach and celery), liver, asparagus, bacon, cheese, coffee, and green tea.	Rare, bleeding into brain in newborn babies.	Fat soluble.	Widely given by injection to babies at birth. Made by intestinal bacteria.

Source: http://www.eatwell.gov.uk

The Food Standards Agency's 8 tips for eating well

It has now been recognised that it is very hard to work out a balanced diet including all the nutrients, so the Food Standards Agency has created eight tips for making healthier choices. The practical tips are aimed to help people to achieve a healthy balanced diet as part of a healthier lifestyle. For anyone who does not need a special diet, these should provide a diet containing all the nutrients needed, and should reduce the risk of developing diet-related illnesses such as heart disease, anaemia, constipation and some cancers.

1. Base your meals on starchy foods.
2. Eat lots of fruit and veg.
3. Eat more fish – including a portion of oily fish per week.
4. Cut down on saturated fat and sugar.
5. Try to eat less salt – no more than 6g a day.
6. Get active and try to be a healthy weight.
7. Drink plenty of water.
8. Don't skip breakfast.

Activity 24

Access the Eat Well website: www.eatwell.gov.uk. It has a lot of information about healthy eating, including different dietary requirements at different ages, food hygiene information, and conditions requiring special diets. Have a go at the quizzes and games, or just explore the website.

If you are not keen on using the Internet, or don't have access to a computer, you can get leaflets about the Eat Well, Be Well initiative from Food Standards Agency Publications on 0845 606 0667. Alternatively, you could try your local health centre or library.

1. What medical conditions are less common in cultures that eat more unsaturated fats than saturated fats?
2. Which carbohydrates should people eat more of and which should they eat less of?
3. What is a trace element?
4. What function does vitamin A perform?

Part of your job as a care worker may be to purchase food on
behalf of, or with, your service users. You may need to advise
them about the benefits of buying fresh, frozen or processed
foods, so you need to know how different ways of preserving food
affect its nutritional value.

What you need to learn

- Fresh foods.
- Frozen foods.
- Processed food.
- Nutritional values.
- Cost and value for money.
- Supporting individuals to work within budgets.

Fresh foods

We associate fresh food with health, but this is only true if it is
eaten soon after purchase. Although old vegetables will not usually
cause food poisoning, and still provide fibre, their vitamin content
starts to diminish as they age. Buying more fresh food than a
service user needs will either mean that they will be eating

poor-quality food, or that they will have to throw some away. This is a waste of money for someone who may be on a low income. If people are unable to purchase fresh vegetables every day or two, it may be better to freeze them, or buy commercially frozen vegetables. Supermarkets often package fresh meat and vegetables in larger packs than a person living alone needs. It is usually more economical to buy loose vegetables, so you can buy just the amount that is needed. Butchers will serve small quantities of meat. Many supermarkets have a butcher's counter, although you will have to queue. Local butchers are often very helpful, but can be more expensive.

Frozen foods

Frozen foods are the best alternative to fresh foods, and they are convenient to use, since they require little preparation. Frozen-food manufacturers freeze food quickly at its peak condition, so its nutrient content is preserved. It is important not to let the food defrost between buying it and putting it in the freezer at home. Freezing does not kill bacteria, it just stops them reproducing, so once food starts to defrost, bacteria, if present, can start to multiply again. Frozen foods are preserved without using additives; food additives in the UK have undergone stringent testing and are considered safe, however some, such as E102, known as tartrazine, have been linked to hyperactivity in children, though this is not yet proven. Fresh vegetables can be frozen at home to preserve their vitamin content.

Activity 25

Have a go at freezing some fresh vegetables to use at a later date.

Put the freezer onto 'fast freeze'.

To keep vegetables in peak condition, you will have to clean and trim them and heat a pan of water until it is boiling. Leave the heat on full, as when you put the vegetables into the water it will go off the boil. Bring back to the boil and then leave to boil for a few minutes. This varies with different vegetables, for example medium-stem broccoli needs 4 minutes, small Brussels sprouts 3 minutes, slices of courgette need 1 minute. This is called blanching: it kills bacteria, but preserves vitamins, colour, texture and flavour. For further information on freezing fresh vegetables you could consult a freezer cookery book or http://www.allotment.org.uk/allotment_foods/Storing_the_Surplus_Freezing.php.

When the vegetables have been boiled for the correct length of time, remove them from the boiling water and plunge them into cold water for 5 seconds, then transfer them to another bowl of cold water with ice cubes in it.

When the food is cold, drain it and put it in freezer bags. Store these in the freezer until required, then cook them as you would frozen vegetables bought from the supermarket.

Compare the results for taste, cost and convenience.

Processed food

Food does not go off in cans because once the can is sealed it is heated to a very high temperature to kill any bacteria that may be inside. Canned food has been criticised as being less nutritious than fresh food, and often having a high salt or sugar content. However, many manufacturers have responded to these criticisms and it is possible to buy fish and vegetables in spring water and fruit in natural juice. Canned food does not deteriorate for years, so it is better to eat canned foods than fresh vegetables that are deteriorating, or meat past its use-by date. It is worth remembering, however, that on rare occasions cans may 'blow'. This may happen either when bacterial spores inside the can germinate and produce gas, or when acid in the food reacts with the metal of the can, producing hydrogen gas.

Vacuum-packed foods include bacon and fish. The majority of bacteria found in food need air to reproduce, so vacuum packing will slow down the rate at which food will go off. Vacuum-packed foods can often be kept in the fridge for two or three weeks, so are a good standby in case a carer is unable to visit. The fridge should be kept below 3°C for these foods, as this will prevent bacteria that can breed without air from multiplying. Vacuum-packed foods can be preserved in other ways, such as being heated for a short while, or being preserved in salt solution.

Ready meals can be a useful standby for a service user who is unable to spend a long time preparing meals. They can be chilled, frozen or even ultra-heat treated (UHT). Several companies specialise in delivering ready meals to elderly and disabled service users who live in their own homes. This can be a good alternative to meals-on-wheels for those who are able to prepare meals for themselves. It gives the service user more choice and control over their diet as they can choose from a large selection of meals. Most of these meals can be cooked in a microwave.

Nutritional values

As well as the way food is stored and preserved, the way food is cooked can also affect its nutritional value. Fresh vegetables served raw have a high nutritional value. Cooking vegetables destroys some of the vitamins, but some cooking methods cause less damage than others. When vegetables are boiled the vitamins are lost into the water, and the longer they are boiled the more vitamins are lost. A study carried out by Professor Paul Thornalley at Warwick University, published in 2007, found that the anti-cancer substances in green vegetables are much reduced by boiling.

If you use the vegetable water to make gravy, you can save some of the vitamins. However, vegetables that are steamed instead of boiled retain much of their nutritional value. Stir-frying is also a good cooking method for retaining vitamins, and requires only a minimal amount of fat. Another way of retaining the vitamins of vegetables is to cook them in a casserole with meat: the goodness stays in the gravy.

Frying food retains nutrients, and dry frying (frying without fat) is a useful method if you wish to have a quick meal.

The nutritional value of food is depleted by keeping food hot, so whenever possible food should be served as soon as it is cooked.

Activity 26

Look at the menu below, and think how you could improve the nutritional value of the meal by substituting foods, changing the way it is prepared or using ingredients differently preserved.

- Tinned vegetable soup
- Fried bacon chops, boiled carrots and broccoli, chips
- Tinned fruit salad and evaporated milk.

Food labelling

Foods other than loose foods, such as vegetables, should have their nutritional value displayed on their label. This should explain the number of calories and the amount of protein, fat and carbohydrates provided per serving and per 100g, and will state how much a 'serving' weighs for that product. Some also list the vitamins and minerals found in that food, and the percentage of recommended daily amount (RDA) provided. If you want to compare one product with another, use the amount per 100g on each product to compare.

Food labels, by law, must state: the name of the food, the ingredients listed in order of weight, with the main ingredient first, additives and preservatives, 'use-by' and 'best-before' dates, storage information, and batch number.

Many manufacturers will include information about ingredients that some people are allergic or intolerant to, such as nuts, lactose and gluten.

The tables below contain examples of the information you would expect to find for Cereal A and Cereal B

Cereal A

Typical values		Per 100g		Per 30g serving with 125ml of semi-skimmed milk	
Energy		370kcal		168kcal	
Protein		8.0g		6.5g	
Carbohydrate		69.2g		26.8g	
of which sugars		26.5g		13.9g	
Fat		6.6g		4.0g	
of which saturates		3.6g		2.4g	
Fibre		7.7g		2.3g	
Sodium		0.29g		0.16g	
equivalent as salt		0.7g		0.4g	
Vitamins & minerals		%RDA			%RDA
Vit B$_1$	1.2mg	85%	0.4mg		29%
Vit B$_2$	1.4mg	85%	0.6mg		40%
Vit B$_3$	15.3mg	85%	4.7mg		26%
Vit B$_5$	5.1mg	85%	1.9mg		32%
Vit B$_6$	1.7mg	85%	0.6mg		29%
Vit B$_9$	170 µg	85%	59µg		29%
Vit B$_{12}$	0.9µg	85%	0.8µg		76%
Iron	11.8mg	85%	3.6mg		26%

Cereal B

Typical values		Per 100g		Per 30g serving with 125ml of semi-skimmed milk	
Energy		326kcal		156kcal	
Protein		10.8g		7.4g	
Carbohydrate		66.7g		26.0g	
of which sugars		17.2g		11.1g	
Fat		1.8g		2.5g	
of which saturates		0.4g		1.3g	
Fibre		13.6g		4.1g	
Sodium		0.57g		0.24g	
equivalent as salt		1.4g		0.6g	
Vitamins & minerals		%RDA			%RDA
Vit B$_1$	1.6mg	115%	0.4mg		38%
Vit B$_2$	0.8mg	115%	0.8mg		49%
Vit B$_3$	20.7mg	115%	6.3mg		35%
Vit B$_5$	6.9mg	115%	2.5mg		41%
Vit B$_6$	2.3mg	115%	0.8mg		38%
Vit B$_9$	230 µg	115%	77µg		38%
Vit B$_{12}$	1.2µg	115%	0.8µg		85%
Iron	16.1mg	115%	4.9mg		35%

Activity 27

Look at the nutrition tables on page 101. Which product would be best for:

- someone who is suffering from iron-deficiency anaemia?
- someone who is constipated?
- someone who is trying to lose weight?
- someone who has high blood pressure?

Food labels also allow people to make choices about the food they eat. If a person is trying to choose a healthy diet, they need to know whether food is high or low in different components, and what this means.

	High per 100g	Low per 100g
Sugars	15g	5g
Fat	20g	3g
Saturated fat	5g	1.5g
Salt	1.5g	0.3g
Sodium	0.6g	0.1g

Source: Food Standards Agency

Some food manufacturers make claims about the health benefits of their products. There are rules governing this. Manufacturers cannot call foods 'reduced calorie', for example, unless they are much lower in calories than the standard version. There are no legal definitions for terms such as 'low fat', however producers would not be allowed to describe high-fat food as 'low fat'.

If a food label has an image of an ingredient, that ingredient must be contained in the food. For example, if a yogurt carton has a picture of blackberries on it, there must be blackberries, not just flavouring, in the yogurt.

Organic foods are produced according to certain standards. In the case of organic crops, it means they were grown without the use of pesticides or artificial fertilisers or sludge from sewage treatment plants. Such foods must not be preserved with food additives. Animals reared for organic meat must not be given growth hormone or antibiotics unless they are ill. Organic produce is not genetically modified. There is no conclusive evidence that organic food has any health advantages over non-organic foods, but research into this continues.

Supporting individuals to work within budgets

You may work with service users who are living on a limited budget. They may ask you to do some shopping for them, or you may take them shopping. Not all healthy foods are expensive, so you may be able to advise service users on healthy foods that they can afford. Chicken and pork tend to be cheaper than beef and lamb; they are also healthier, being lower in fat.

Larger supermarkets often produce own-label products with similar nutritional values to branded products. Some supermarkets have two ranges of own-label products, with the more expensive one usually being of a similar quality to the branded ones. Budget own-label foods are sometimes higher in fat, salt and sugar, with poorer quality ingredients. However, some of the budget own-label foods are still nutritious, such as raw chicken breast. Unprocessed foods from the budget range, such as raw meat and vegetables, are usually a good buy.

Activity 28

Go to the supermarket.

1. Look at the labels on a range of similar foods to compare their nutritional value, for example choose three types of biscuits, including one that claims to be a healthy option. Look at the values for 100g rather than per biscuit, as this will give a fair comparison. Look at the fat content – both saturated and unsaturated – and the carbohydrate content, including sugars.

   Did your findings surprise you?

2. Compare the price and nutritional value of three similar products from different ranges of food: economy, own label and branded.

   Do you think the common idea that budget foods are less healthy is correct? It may depend on the food you have chosen.

Bulk buying can save a lot of money, as long as the food stays edible until the person wants to eat it. For example, you should be wary of encouraging a service user to buy an economy-sized bag of fresh fruit or vegetables, unless they are going to freeze them, whereas a multi-pack of tinned tuna will last for a year or two. Likewise, potatoes will go off whereas pasta and rice will last a long time. If several service users live together they could bulk-buy if they all like similar foods. Special offers can help small budgets, too.

Take a calculator with you when you take your service users out shopping, to work out which products provide the best value for money. Don't forget to check the nutritional value as well.

Activity 29

Look at the three product sizes and prices below, and work out which is the best value for money.

Leading brand tuna in spring water 185g 4 tins for	Own label tuna in spring water 185g	Leading brand tuna in brine 400g
£3.38	48p	£1.00

Often the price per 100g is displayed on the shelf below each product, making it easier to compare prices.

1. Why should fresh vegetables be eaten as soon as possible after purchase?
2. Which are the most nutritious, fresh or frozen vegetables?
3. Why has the nutritional value of canned fruit and vegetables been criticised in the past?
4. What have food producers done to address this criticism?
5. Why are boiled vegetables less nutritious than steamed vegetables?

3.3 Understand the importance of appropriate storage of food and drink

To keep food in good condition it should be stored correctly: in the right place, at the right temperature and for the right length of time. It is important that you understand where foods should be stored to prevent food poisoning, and to prevent attracting vermin to food-storage areas.

What you need to learn

How to store food in a:

- refrigerator
- freezer
- dry cupboard
- larder.

Refrigerator

Chilled foods should be kept cool when being transported from the shop, by using a cool bag with ice blocks. Put the food into the fridge as soon as possible.

Fresh and cooked meats and dairy produce should always be kept in a fridge. The fridge temperature should be between 1°C and to 4°C to be safe. You can use a fridge thermometer to keep a check on the temperature inside a fridge. Fresh meat should be kept on the bottom shelf of the fridge and should not be used after the 'use-by' date. Remember that meat from a butcher will not have a use-by date. The table below gives some guidance about how long meat can be stored in the refrigerator.

Uncooked	In a fridge	Cooked	In a fridge
Joints of beef, pork and lamb	3 days	Joints	2 days
Steaks	2 days	Chicken	2 days
Chops	2 days	Chicken, stuffed	2 days
Chicken (whole or portions)	2 days	Casseroles	2 days
Bacon rashers (vacuum packed)	10 days	Ham	2 days
Cubed meat	1 day	Meat pies	1 day
Minced meat	1 day	Sliced meat	2 days
Liver, heart and kidneys	1 day	Paté	2 days
Sausages	3 days		

Source: http://www.foster-uk.com

When putting food into the fridge, check the food that is already there. Remove and discard any that has passed its use-by date, and move to the front any foods that need using up, to ensure they are not wasted. Refrigeration slows down the speed at which bacteria breed, but food will still go off in a fridge. Although vegetables and eggs do not have to be refrigerated, they will last longer and keep fresher if kept in the fridge.

Some foods have a tendency to go mouldy: cheese, bread, jam and fruit are particularly prone to this. Once mould has developed the food should be thrown away, as mould produces toxins that penetrate into the food, and can cause illness.

The correct storage of food in a fridge will help prevent contamination, keep food fresh and avoid waste

Freezer

The freezer should be kept at -18°C. This will stop bacteria from breeding. Even when commercially frozen food has passed its 'best-before' date it will not cause food poisoning, however it probably won't taste as good as it should.

The recommended maximum freezing time for the main food groups are:

- vegetables 15–18 months
- meat and poultry 6–12 months
- fish 4–10 months.

This is only a rough guide and you should follow the advice on the packaging. Meat and poultry may oxidise and go rancid. Anything with a high water content, such as lettuce or cucumber, will become soggy when thawed, and eggs will burst out of their shells. Foods that are not properly wrapped may dehydrate (freezer burn). Many fridge iceboxes and freezers have a star rating, indicating how cold they are.

*	- 6°C
**	-12°C
***	-18°C
****	below -18°C

The packaging of some commercially frozen foods gives information about how long the food should be kept, based on the star rating on the fridge or freezer.

Some foods, for example vegetables and pizzas, can be cooked straight from frozen but others, such as frozen chicken, should be thawed before cooking. It is important to follow the manufacturer's instructions to avoid food poisoning and to ensure that food is cooked properly. Once frozen food has been thawed it should be treated as fresh and must not be frozen again, unless it has subsequently been cooked, such as in a casserole. When buying frozen foods you should try to prevent the food defrosting before getting it to the service user's home. This can be done by waiting until the end of your shopping trip before taking frozen foods out of the freezer, or transporting them in a cool box.

Larder/dry cupboard

Canned and packet foods should be kept in a dry cupboard to prevent tins from rusting and packets from getting damp and spoiling the contents. Some products, such as UHT milk and tinned foods, can be kept at room temperature until they have been opened, but after being opened they should be put into the fridge. Leftover tinned food should be transferred to another container, not left in the can. Again, check use-by dates regularly and bring older foods to the front of the shelves and put foods with a longer shelf-life to the back.

1. What temperature should the fridge be set to?

2. Where should raw meat be stored?

3. What happens to frozen foods after reaching the 'best-before' date?

4. How can you prevent frozen foods thawing out between the shop and the care setting?

5. If you only use half a can of food, what should you do with the remainder if it is being saved for another meal?

Cooking methods can be chosen for various reasons, including health benefits, taste, cooking equipment available, and time available. In this section you will learn about the benefits of different cooking methods.

What you need to learn

You need to know the appropriate methods of cooking for the care setting and the needs of the individual.

- Cooking methods.
- Keeping food hot.

Cooking methods

Grilling and frying

When you grill foods the fat drips down into the pan beneath, whereas fried foods are bathed in fat, which is then likely to be served with the food. Frying should be avoided whenever possible for all service users, especially those who are overweight. If you do fry foods, use unsaturated oil, such as sunflower, corn or olive oil, rather than lard, which is a saturated fat. Whatever you choose, use as little oil as possible, to keep the calorie content down. Frying is a very quick way of cooking food, which might be a reason for using this method; however grilling doesn't take much longer.

Deep-fat frying should be avoided as a lot of fat is absorbed into foods, increasing their **calorific value** significantly.

calorific value

the number of calories a food contains

Sometimes a recipe suggests frying meat to seal it, before adding gravy to braise or casserole it. You don't need to use fat to do this, as the fat is naturally in the meat and will emerge in the frying. You may need to use a little oil for sealing very low-fat meat, such as chicken breast. Always drain off excess fat before adding the gravy.

You need to take special care with service users who are confused or liable to forget the frying pan or grill are on, as fires can start quickly when cooking with fat.

Stir-frying

Stir-frying is a fast way to cook vegetables and strips of meat, poultry and fish, and retains the vitamins in vegetables. You should use only a very small amount of oil over a high heat. You can use a wok or a frying pan to stir-fry.

Steaming and microwaving

These are the healthiest ways to cook vegetables. You can also cook fish, sliced ham and bacon by steaming. You can steam food by placing it in a steamer pan over a pan of boiling water. Care must be taken with service users' safety, however. A safer alternative would be an electric or microwave steamer. Make sure the water is hot before you put the food in the steamer. Fish can be steamed by putting it between two heat-resistant plates over a pan of water. The juices can then be used to make a sauce. The fish can be served with brightly coloured and strong-flavoured vegetables to make the meal taste interesting and look attractive.

To microwave vegetables, use a small amount of water and cook for 2–3 minutes.

Ideally, vegetables should be cooked so that they are slightly crunchy when eaten, though some people find this unappealing. If they are cooked until soft, there will be little goodness left in them. For those with chewing problems you can use a food processor to chop them finely, without losing the nutritional benefits of not overcooking.

Microwaves can also be used to cook ready meals or reheat chilled foods; this reduces preparation time. This is useful if you work in the community and need to prepare something in a short time. It is essential that the instructions are followed precisely to ensure that all bacteria are killed.

Steaming is particularly suitable for service users who live at home and are cooking for themselves, as long as they can safely manage pans of boiling water, or an electric or microwave steamer. In a residential care setting where there are many service users to cook for, large steamers would be used. Microwaves tend to be suitable for smaller quantities, but might be useful for preparing special diets if only one or two service users have that particular choice. Some meats do not cook well in a microwave, particularly beef, which can be very tough if cooked in this way.

Poaching

Poaching means cooking in a pan of liquid just below boiling point. It is a healthy way to cook and can be used for fish, chicken and eggs. Poached food can taste bland, but you can add flavourings such as herbs and seasonings to the poaching liquid.

Roasting

Roasting involves cooking food by dry heat in an oven, or on a spit, usually with added fat, although fatty meat can be roasted without extra fat. If meat is laid on a metal rack over a roasting tin, the fat can drip into the tin, so that less fat is served with the meat.

Roasting enhances the flavour of foods. Roasting in olive oil is the healthiest method, as olive oil contains fat-soluble vitamins and unsaturated fats, which can decrease levels of the 'bad' cholesterol in blood, and increase the levels of the type that gives protection against heart disease. It will increase the calorific value, however. Roasting is suitable in all care settings, as long as there is an oven. Peppers and parsnips roast particularly well.

Baking

Baking involves cooking foods such as bread, cakes and jacket potatoes in an oven, without the fat that is used in roasting. This creates steam, which combines with the dry heat and cooks the food. Ham, chicken and fish can also be baked in foil. Products have been developed to reduce the amount of saturated fat in cakes and pastries, for example white fat made from sunflower oil. Some recipes use fruit purée in place of some of the fat in a recipe, to reduce the fat content.

Casseroling

Casseroles can be very healthy. Lean meat should be used, which should be fried without using fat to seal it. Low-salt gravy mix can be added and lots of vegetables, beans or pulses. You could even add rice or potatoes to make it a complete meal. The longer you leave the casserole in the oven, the more tender the meat will be. A casserole can be put in the oven for a service user living at home to serve for themselves later in the day, as long as they can get the casserole out of the oven without burning themselves. A slow cooker is an alternative. These usually sit on the work surface, so are easier to serve from. If there is fat on the top of the casserole, skim this off. If you cook a casserole the day before and refrigerate it, you can easily remove the fat from the gravy before thoroughly reheating it until it is piping hot. You could use a food thermometer to ensure that it has reached 70°C before serving.

Do you cook meals for yourself in the healthiest ways? Try different cooking methods to see if you can improve your own diet. Once you are confident, you could work with service users to choose healthier cooking methods.

Keeping food hot

You should avoid hot-holding if at all possible, but if it cannot be avoided the food must be kept at 63°C or higher to ensure that bacteria do not multiply. You should also cover the food so that it doesn't dry out. A bain-marie is a piece of equipment for keeping food hot. It contains very hot water and stainless steel compartments to place food in. It will keep food hot without boiling or overcooking. If food is being kept hot on a cooker ring, check regularly to make sure there is still enough water and add more if not. You will need to do this if the service user is not available, or is not ready to eat at the planned mealtime.

1. Which are the healthiest ways of cooking food?
2. If you have to use cooking oil, what are the healthier types of oil to use?
3. What is the most important thing to remember about reheating food?
4. Above what temperature should food be held if being kept hot?

4 Legislation relevant to providing food and drink

4.1 Understand the legislation, regulations and guidance that govern nutrition and food preparation and handling

It is very important that you understand and work within the law. If you do not, you could lose your job, the organisation you work for could be closed temporarily or permanently, or you could be prosecuted. The laws you are expected to follow are designed to keep service users, staff and visitors safe, and to ensure that service users are cared for in a way that reflects good practice. Service users should feel respected and valued, and care values should be upheld.

What you need to learn

- Health and Safety at Work Act 1974.
- Management of Health and Safety at Work Act (amended 1994 and 1999).
- Food Safety Act 1990.
- The Food Safety (General Food Hygiene) Regulations (Department of Health 1995).
- Human Rights Act 1998.
- Care Standards Act 2000.
- Health Act 1999.
- NHS Community Care Act 1990.
- Mental Health Act 1983 and the Mental Health Bill 2006.
- Data Protection Act 1998.
- Disability Discrimination Act 1995 and 2005.
- National Service Framework for Older People 2001.
- RCN guidelines – Clinical Study 17 'Recipe for Change'.

Health and Safety at Work Act 1974

This is the main law that affects the workplace, putting responsibility on both employers and employees to protect the health and safety of each other and of service users and visitors to the setting. As this law is over 30 years old, many new regulations have been brought in, such as The Food Safety (General Food Hygiene) Regulations (Department of Health 1995).

Activity 30

Complete the table below by providing one example for each of the responsibilities relevant to providing food and drink.

Employer's responsibilities	
Carry out risk assessments	
Ensure health and safety regulations are observed	
Provide safety equipment	
Record all accidents and incidents	
Ensure workplace is fully insured	
Ensure staff are properly trained	
Employee's responsibilities	
Use any equipment provided properly	
Report hazards	
Take care of own and other people's health and safety	
Attend health and safety training	
Follow policies and procedures	

Management of Health and Safety at Work Act (amended 1994 and 1999)

This law was amended in 1994 and again in 1999. The main focus is on prevention of illness and injury by carrying out risk assessments and changing the work done by staff to lessen the chance that any harm comes to employees.

The main points are that employers should:

1. Avoid risks to staff.

2. Assess thoroughly any risks that cannot be avoided.

3. Find the root cause of any risk and try to remove the danger.

4. Change the way work is done to make it safer for the staff.

5. Keep up to date with new technology.

6. Replace dangerous substances and procedures by non-dangerous or less dangerous ones.

7. Produce a policy that covers equipment, working methods, working conditions, and staff relationships.

8. One person's health and safety must not be seen as more important than the overall health and safety of the whole workforce.

9. Ensure that clear instructions are given to staff.

Activity 31

Match the safety measures below to the points above.

Point no.	Safety measure
	(a) The manager has just bought some new silicone oven gloves that can be used when cooking with service users to reduce the risk of burns.
	(b) A risk assessment has been carried out on cooking with service users.
	(c) A training session is given to all staff about using the meat slicer.
	(d) The manager has issued a comprehensive health and safety policy covering all aspects of work at the setting.
	(e) An investigation into the number of scalds in the kitchen resulted in the refitting of the kitchen so that the sink is nearer the cooker.
	(f) A food processor has been bought to slice vegetables more safely.
	(g) The anti-bacterial hand wash was not changed, despite one member of staff being allergic to it, as other products are not as effective. That member of staff has been moved to another job.
	(h) A new food thermometer has been purchased that sounds an alarm if the temperature of the food being kept hot falls to 63°C.
	(i) There is a one-way system in the kitchen to prevent staff running into each other.

Food Safety Act 1990

Under the Food Safety Act 1990 any food provided must be fit to eat. Any establishment breaching food-hygiene standards can be served a notice of improvement by an environmental health officer, and can, in extreme circumstances, be closed temporarily or permanently if practices are considered to be a health hazard. Businesses can be prosecuted for breaching standards.

The Food Safety (General Food Hygiene) Regulations (Department of Health 1995)

The Food Safety (General Food Hygiene) Regulations 1995 aim to prevent cases of food poisoning by ensuring that:

- food areas are kept clean and good standards of personal hygiene are maintained
- foods are cooked thoroughly
- foods are kept at the right temperature
- cross-contamination is prevented.

Activity 32

Look back at the advice given about food hygiene in Sections 2.3 and 3.3. What is done at your place of work to ensure that service users are not put at risk of food poisoning?

Human Rights Act 1998

The Human Rights Act 1998 is based on the European Convention on Human Rights. As well as protecting people against serious abuse and life-threatening situations, it also protects our rights in everyday life, such as the right to practise our beliefs and live the life we wish, as long as it doesn't infringe other people's rights.

Your human rights are:

- the right to life
- freedom from torture and degrading treatment
- freedom from slavery and forced labour
- the right to liberty
- the right to a fair trial
- the right not to be punished for something that wasn't a crime when you did it
- the right to respect for private and family life
- freedom of thought, conscience and religion
- freedom of expression
- freedom of assembly and association

- the right to marry or form a civil partnership and start a family
- the right not to be discriminated against in respect of these rights and freedoms
- the right to own property
- the right to an education
- the right to participate in free elections.

For further information on human rights, see www.direct.gov.uk.

It is the right of service users to be able to follow their chosen diet, whether for religious or moral reasons. They have the right to eat in private if they prefer. If service users need assistance with eating, this should be done in a way that is not degrading, therefore clothes should be protected from spilt food, but not by using a bib, such as would be used for a baby, but by using a napkin or an apron.

Care Standards Act 2000

The Care Standards Act replaced the Registered Homes Act 1984. In 2003 the Health and Social Care (Community Health and Standards) Act made some slight amendments.

The Care Standards Act sets out minimum standards of care that should be provided in care settings, with standards for different types of provision, such as residential settings for older people and adults with disabilities, and people cared for in their own homes. The Commission for Social Care Inspection (CSCI) inspect care settings to ensure that minimum standards of care are provided.

A CSCI inspection report includes information about the meals provided similar to the following:

> On the day of the inspection the main meal was roast chicken, stuffing, creamed potatoes, cabbage and carrots. Alternative choices were cheese salad or jacket potato. The meal appeared appetising and residents were seen enjoying it. The menu record showed that meals are nutritious and varied, with a choice always available.

Health Act 1999

The Health Act 1999 enables care to be provided to one service user in the best way to meet needs, by each care provider funding the part of the care that they would previously have provided. For example, if a service user needs assistance with meals, this might be funded by social services, but it could make more sense for a home care assistant from a private agency to cook the meal whilst at the service user's home doing the housework. The funding for the provision of the meal would still come from social services.

The aim is to enable partners to join together to design and deliver services around the needs of users, rather than worrying about the limits of their organisations. These arrangements should help remove gaps in services and prevent overlap.

The NHS and Community Care Act 1990

The NHS and Community Care Act 1990 made it a duty for local authorities to assess individuals for the care and support they need and decide how care can best be provided. This might be in a residential or nursing home, or in their own home with a package of care designed to meet their needs, so they are safe and well. In order to ensure that service users eat and drink properly, the local authority may decide that meals-on-wheels should be provided. It may be more appropriate to organise groceries to be delivered to the door, or to have the kitchen adapted to make it wheelchair accessible.

Mental Health Act 1983 and the Mental Health Bill 2006

The Mental Health Act 1983 made provision for the compulsory admission to hospital of those with mental ill-health, if they were considered to be a danger to themselves or others. The Mental Health Bill 2006 amends the Mental Health Act 1983. A person with anorexia nervosa might be admitted under the Mental Health Act because their weight has fallen to a dangerously low level, and the person needs to be fed through a tube to save their life.

Data Protection Act 1998

The Data Protection Act 1998 relates to personal information held in paper and electronic format. Information held should be relevant and not excessive. It should have been obtained for lawful reasons and should be accurate and current. The information should not be held for longer than is necessary. Information should be protected against unauthorised access and accidental destruction. People are entitled to view any data held about them.

Disability Discrimination Acts 1995 and 2005

The Disability Discrimination Act 1995 made it illegal to refuse to supply goods or provide services or facilities to a person just because they are disabled. It is also illegal to deliberately make it difficult for a person with a disability to access goods, services and facilities. The Disability Discrimination Act 2005 requires equality of opportunity to be actively promoted and discrimination eliminated for people with disabilities.

National Service Framework for Older People

National Service Frameworks are standards that have to be met by health and social care services.

The four target areas are:

- rooting out age discrimination
- providing person-centred care
- promoting the health and independence of older people
- applying evidence-based best practice.

With regard to nutrition and well-being, older people may, for example, need specialist advice on a healthy diet because they have been told they have diabetes or high cholesterol, or they just want to reduce the risk of developing cancer and heart disease. This is to increase the chance that older people can continue to lead healthy and fulfilling lives. Health promotion activities should take into account the cultural background of service users.

Although it is not stated in the National Service Frameworks, health promotion activities should also consider the gender, education and income of individuals, to ensure that advice given is meaningful and likely to be something they can relate to, as this will increase the likelihood that the advice will be followed. For more information on health promotion activities, see www.dh.gov.uk.

National Minimum Standards for Care Homes

Standard 15 of the National Minimum Standards for Care Homes for Older People requires the registered manager to ensure that service users receive a varied, appealing, wholesome and nutritious diet that is suited to individuals' assessed and recorded requirements, and that meals are taken in a pleasant setting and at flexible times.

Service users should be offered a choice of three meals a day, at least one of which should be cooked. Drinks and snacks should always be available. Foods should be nicely presented and appetising. Special diets should be catered for, including religious and cultural diets. Menus should be available in different formats. Diet should be assessed on admission and recorded on the care plan.

Staff should be ready to offer assistance if needed, maintaining service users' independence and dignity as much as possible.

The following is adapted from the National Minimum Standards for Care Homes for Older People, published by the Department of Health in 2002.

Residents think food is very important to their quality of life. It is important to their health and well-being. If a resident is unable to eat – due to disability, depression, because there isn't enough food or because food is of poor quality – they can become very ill. Staff should watch each resident's food intake, without making it too obvious. In order to ensure that residents receive a good diet, food must be of good quality, tempting, and available whenever the resident needs to eat or drink.

Eating is a social part of life and residents should be able to continue to prepare food and drink if they are able and wish to do so. If the kitchen isn't safe for residents to use, other facilities should be offered.

Personal and cultural/religious food preferences should be respected, including providing food that has been slaughtered and prepared in accordance with religious requirements. False claims about this must not be made.

You can find more out about National Minimum Standards for different service user groups by accessing http://www.csci.org.uk/professional/care_providers/all_services/national_minimum_standards.aspx.

According to CSCI, in 2005 one care home in six failed to achieve the minimum standard for providing food and drink. There were 453 complaints upheld between April 2004 and October 2005. The main reasons for the complaints were poor quality (28%), poor choice (16%), and limited availability of food (27%) (Valios, 2007).

Skills for Care Knowledge Set

The Knowledge Set for Nutrition and Well-being you are currently studying is part of a series of knowledge sets that have been devised to raise standards in care settings. These set out the minimum level of understanding that staff working in the care sector should have.

RCN guidelines – Clinical Study 17 'Recipe for Change'

In 2000 the *Nursing Times* and Nestlé produced a study unit endorsed by the Royal College of Nursing to improve nursing staff's understanding of the nutritional requirements of older people in hospital, nursing homes and in their own homes. The video and accompanying notes provide useful information about causes of, and strategies to prevent, undernutrition and overnutrition.

Health-care workers can and should play a central role in **nutritional screening** of those who are malnourished or likely to become malnourished. Older people should be screened soon after they come under the care of health-care workers. Weight is not necessarily an accurate means of identifying poor nutrition, as it can give a false impression. Fluid retention, for example, will increase weight.

The clinical study unit suggests other ways to assess nutritional status, such as measuring the circumference of the arms and calf muscles. Weight loss might be indicated if clothes are obviously too big. Asking service users what they normally eat can reveal poor dietary intake, such as relying on snacks.

nutritional screening

a simple and rapid process of identifying risk factors known to be linked to malnutrition

1. Which laws are intended to protect service users from food poisoning?
2. Under which law do service users have a right to a special diet if they need one?
3. At what point would someone with anorexia nervosa be forcibly admitted to hospital under the Mental Health Act?
4. What are the standards for the provision of food and drink as set out in the National Minimum Standards for Care Homes for Older People?

4.2 Understand the organisation's policies and procedures with regard to nutrition and well-being, food and drink preparation and presentation

The Department of Health guidance for Care Homes for Adults (18–65) states that care homes must develop policies, procedures or codes of practice on food safety, nutrition and food hygiene.

Care settings must keep detailed records so that an inspector can tell that the diet served is nutritious and that special diets are catered for. In addition, records must be kept to show that good food hygiene is practised.

One example of safe practice an environmental health officer may wish to monitor is the temperature at which foods are held between cooking and serving. If it is written down every time on a chart then this record can be shown to an inspector to show that good standards are being maintained.

Date & Time	Signature	Temp °C
16/09/07 13.05hrs	C.J. Aldworth	65°C

What you need to learn

- Organisational policies.
- Food and nutrition policies.
- Budget concerns.
- Food hygiene policy

Organisational policies

Every organisation has to devise policies appropriate to the type of setting, the service user group and any relevant factors that influence the food provided. You should access these and make sure you are familiar with their requirements.

Food and nutrition policies

Food and nutrition policies are intended to ensure that service users receive a diet that meets their nutritional needs, including providing for those who are malnourished when they begin to receive care and those who need a special diet for medical reasons or personal preference.

Food and nutrition policies cover topics such as:

- assessment of nutritional needs
- referral of those who are at risk of poor nutrition
- minimum standards that will be expected in the provision of food and drink
- how staff will be trained in good practice
- how information will be recorded.

Budget concerns

One of the most influential factors on the quality of food provided for service users in an organisation is the budget that has been allocated for purchasing food. In 2004 the Joseph Rowntree Foundation estimated that care homes spent on average £2.34 per person per day on food. If this is the policy of a care setting, the food is likely to be of poor quality. Even an increase to £4 per person per day should be ample to provide a really nutritious diet.

Food hygiene policy

A food hygiene policy sets out guidance to prevent cases of food poisoning in a particular setting. The policy should inform staff about measures they need to take to prevent contamination and deterioration of food including:

- food storage
- food preparation
- cleaning procedures
- waste disposal
- personal hygiene
- record keeping
- staff training.

Activity 33

Ask to look at the policies and procedures for your place of work. Find the ones that are relevant to food and drink.

- What do the policies and procedures state you should do in your current job role?
- Are the policies always followed, or do staff cut corners sometimes?
- Can you appreciate the reasons for having policies?

Trainer notes

The following notes are intended to assist in the delivery of the Nutrition and Well-being Knowledge Set. Answers or guidance are provided for all activities, but learners should be encouraged to try to complete the activities without referring to these notes.

As nutrition is such a topical issue, learners may be well informed, so it is advisable to ascertain each learner's level of understanding at the beginning of the programme, to enable you to plan your delivery.

If possible, get access to a care-setting kitchen to include some practical work. Some learners may have done little cooking using raw ingredients, and may need to build up their confidence to enable them to move away from relying on ready meals and processed foods.

Food hygiene could be supported by inviting an environmental health officer to visit. As part of their role involves prevention of food poisoning and food contamination, the EHO should be willing to attend. A food hygiene certificate would be a beneficial qualification for learners to obtain alongside this course.

1. Preparation and presentation of food and drink

1.1 Understand the common factors that affect dietary requirements

This section focuses on the many reasons why service users might receive an inadequate diet and suggests many ways to adapt practice to maximise the chances that service users will receive an adequate diet. The case study at the start of the section could be used to stimulate discussion about experiences that learners have had when they might have been worried about service users' diet and nutrition.

Introduce the positive benefits of well-nourished service users, both to themselves and the staff.

Although most learners will probably be working with adults, particularly the elderly, social care services also cater for children and families, young people and pregnant women, so you should ensure that all age ranges are discussed.

Activity 1

This activity is designed to illustrate that sometimes care workers think they are providing a really good service, but forget about care values. Errol is forgetting about encouraging independence and respecting personal preference. He may have forgotten about religious restrictions. Remember to return to this at the end of the course.

Activity 2

This activity focuses the care worker on their own diet. As care work requires staff to be in good health, a healthy diet is essential.

Care scenario: Donald

This care scenario is not intended to have a right or wrong answer, as it is not an easy problem to solve.

Grief can be impossible to get over for some people, and even those working in the mental health services cannot always return patients to a state where they are functioning as well as they were.

Policies, procedures and job role may restrict the options available. Suggestions could include:

1. Cooking with Donald may increase his confidence in his own ability, and might be an enjoyable activity for him.

2. Trying to persuade him to attend a day centre might be more appropriate, to increase social contact, but not all people wish to attend day centres.

3. It would be nice to take him out for lunch, but there may be health and safety issues preventing this.

Look it up, page 14

This is a straightforward activity to encourage learners to use the Internet. Reasons for constipation include:

- low fibre intake
- dehydration
- immobility
- iron tablets
- morphine-based pain killers
- weakening of bowel muscles in old age.

Activity 3

This activity is intended to encourage learners to apply the information they have been given to similar situations, so it is a good recap activity. Learners may need to look ahead to section 3.1 for dietary sources of nutrients.

Activity 4

This activity may highlight learners' assumptions about what older people like to eat. If you do this in a group session you could compare different learners' answers. The learners themselves may come from a variety of backgrounds, thus giving varied answers to the activity.

Look it up, page 16

Learners are encouraged to widen their understanding to enable them to provide appropriate foods for clients from other cultures.

Activity 5

This activity requires learners to think about the religious restrictions and the food on offer to work out which foods are acceptable. Soup, vegetable curry, fruit salad and baked apples are all OK to offer.

Reflection, page 22

Learners should consider the importance of the social occasion of meals, and decide whether it would be inclusive or embarrassing to be tube fed in front of other service users, or whether PEG feeds should be given in private, but the service user should sit in the dining room when others are eating. Perhaps the group could debate the alternatives.

Activity 6

Learners should write down the timings of the meals and snacks to demonstrate understanding of maintaining stable blood sugar levels. The contents of the menu should follow the guidance given.

Activity 7

Learners can find out about the range of products available for those on special diets, but there is also an opportunity to discuss the fairness of the pricing of such products, and the inconvenience of having to get a prescription.

Activity 8

This is intended to challenge learners to consider how well prepared their workplace is to prevent and deal with sudden severe reactions.

Care scenario: Margaret

This care scenario encourages trainees to consider the difficulties that can exist when dealing with mental ill-health, including deciding the point at which care can be forced upon service users.

Learners should be able to deduce that Margaret's diet is lacking in iron and fibre. Care assistants working with Margaret could be more proactive in encouraging Margaret to do more for herself. The care worker could cook simple meals with Margaret, and discuss higher-fibre foods and foods with a high iron content to see if there are any she does like.

Get the learners to discuss what sort of issues they would be worried about if they visited Margaret. Anything that leaves them concerned about her safety should be reported, as it is better to be safe than sorry. If she refuses, ensure that her husband is able to get help if the situation worsens. Some learners may feel that care should be forced on Margaret if it will make her better, however, it is important that learners appreciate that current practice dictates that it is only in situations where Margaret or her husband are in serious danger that she can be forced to accept care.

Activity 9

This is intended to encourage learners to use their initiative to devise ways to work within care values, even when service users are severely impaired.

Question check

1. Learners should identify food components that are required in greater and lesser quantities at different life stages.
2. Learners should include some of the points on the spider diagram on page 9.
3. Still offer a choice, and consider preferences as well as medical and religious needs.
4. Answers will vary according to practice at individual learners' work places.
5. Learners should include keeping the meal hot enough to prevent bacteria reproducing.

1.2 Understand the importance of the appropriate preparation and presentation of food and drink

This section is designed to emphasise the importance of good food hygiene standards in the prevention of food poisoning. It also covers the importance of presentation in tempting service users to eat well. The case study at the beginning of the section can be discussed with the group to highlight bad practice leading to actual neglect.

Activity 10

This activity could generate some debate about making food too big an issue for children. Some children pick up on parents' anxieties and use food as a tool to control parents.

Care scenario: Patrick, Anthony and Hanif

Learners should be encouraged to use their imagination to develop ways of working around the difficulties caused by learning disabilities. They could make resources, such as a simple recipe book, using symbols.

Activity 11

This is a basic introduction to how policies are devised. Many learners will not be involved in policy-making, but will have to follow policies. It can help them to understand how policies can improve practice and therefore the need to follow policies in the interests of service users' welfare. It can encourage pride in your work and empathy with others.

Question check

1. Learners should show understanding that nice presentation can tempt people to eat. Food should be colourful, and portions should be of a size that will not overwhelm an individual.

2. Several answers should be given, including: before starting to prepare food, after handling raw meat, poultry, fish and eggs, after touching the waste bin, and before touching handles of the fridge, cooker, kettle and kitchen units.

3. Reasons could include swallowing difficulty, poor teeth, sore mouth, during weaning.

4. Learners should show understanding that food for PEG feeding should be specially prepared and sterile, so that the tube does not block and micro-organisms cannot enter the stomach.

5. Encouraging service users to be independent raises self-esteem and self-worth, and enables them to have more control over their lives.

1.3 Understand the importance of creating an appropriate environment in which to eat and drink

Reflection, page 49

Learners are encouraged to think more widely. It is easy to get into a routine and forget that for the service users this routine rules their entire lives. Try to stimulate and challenge learners to be imaginative in providing care, but ensure that they think about health and safety.

Question check

1. Examples might include other service users who have feeding difficulties.
2. Sitting well up, close to the table, in reach of the cutlery, plate of food and drink.
3. Any of: non-slip plate mat; adapted cutlery; scoop dish; lidded mug; plate guard; angled bread knife, jar opener, kettle tipper.
4. Guidelines could include making sure food is hot, but not too hot; encouraging service users to choose from a menu; do not rush them; talk to them, etc.

2. Roles and boundaries

2.1 Understand the role, and responsibilities and boundaries of the worker with regard to following the policies and procedures of the care setting on assessment of dietary requirements

This section gives learners the opportunity to examine their own role and the roles of their colleagues and other members of the multidisciplinary team. This should enable learners to reflect on their own practice, whilst also becoming aware of support available from other sources to improve service users' nutrition.

Reflection, page 55

This aims at stimulating discussion about the difficulties of challenging practice at your place of work. You could discuss strategies that learners could use with senior staff at work.

Statistics have been included to highlight the extent of the problem of poor nutrition in children and the elderly. The Age Concern report 'Hungry to be Heard' is highly recommended, and includes several case studies that could be used as a discussion tool.

There are opportunities for students to really understand and consider why malnutrition occurs, and practical steps that could be taken to improve the diet of service users.

The Malnutrition Universal Screening Tool can be looked at, but further training is needed before carrying out screening with service users.

Activity 12

This activity is intended to inform learners about factors that could indicate a potential for a service user to be malnourished. You could ask learners to bring a copy of the documentation from their workplace to compare.

Question check

1. Learners should show understanding of working around service users' needs and preferences rather than expecting service users to fit into the routine of the setting. Answers could include choice, availability, beliefs and preferences.
2. Learners should include:
   - BMI
   - recent change in weight
   - illness or condition
   - normal dietary intake
   - condition of teeth and mouth
   - ability to provide meals at home.

3. Learners should mention:

- nutritional assessment
- special diet
- assistance required
- record of dietary intake during stay.

2.2 Understand the role, responsibilities and boundaries of the worker in relation to monitoring the condition and therapies of the individual

Learners need to understand the importance of documentation, both for supporting good practice and for legal protection.

Activity 13

This can be used to consolidate learning. Reasons could include:

- doesn't like food offered
- food is cold
- mouth is dry – needs a drink
- hasn't got teeth in
- mouth is sore
- has had enough
- feels ill.

Activity 14

You could extend this activity to get learners to produce leaflets, factsheets or posters.

2.3 Understand the role, responsibilities and boundaries of the worker in relation to food handling and serving

This section will give learners general guidance on food preparation and handling.

Activity 15

It might be better to arrange the EHO to come to a teaching session, than arranging separate visits to each learner's workplace.

Activity 16

This activity encourages learners to think of the causes of poor practice and to be able to think of solutions. Answers could include:

- Follow storage instructions including 'use-by' and 'eat-by' dates
- Cook food thoroughly, especially meat, ensuring that it is cooked through to the middle
- Keep cooked food away from raw food
- Wash salads, fruit and raw vegetables thoroughly before eating
- Wash hands, knives, and cutting boards after handling uncooked food
- Make sure that the refrigerator is at 8°C
- When heating food in a microwave, follow heating and standing times recommended by the manufacturer
- Throw away leftover reheated food
- Cooked food that is not going to be eaten immediately should be quickly cooled and then put into the refrigerator.

Question check

1. Learners should identify:
   - To have evidence in the event of a subsequent enquiry
   - To ensure it is noticed if a service user refuses meals frequently or persistently.

2. Care workers should report:
   - refusal to eat
   - signs of abdominal pain
   - difficulty chewing
   - a rash or breathing difficulties.

3. Learners should realise that their role does not demand that they solve all the problems they encounter. However, as they are in close, regular contact with service users, they are in a good position to observe and report any problems they see to a more experienced member of staff.

Activity 17

This activity could be discussed with the group together, to compare practice between different settings. It does not matter if different care settings use different colour coding, as long as a system is in place. For those learners who work in service users' own homes, the system is not usually necessary, as long as there is only one person involved in the cooking, as they will know what the board was last used for, so contamination should not occur.

Activity 18

This practical activity can help learners practise ways of standing back and encouraging independence in service users.

Activity 19

Learners can explore how service users feel about being assisted with meals, and think how the individual can maintain some control over their lives, and how important this is.

Question check

1. Answers could include:
   - touching cooked food with raw meat
   - not washing your hands
   - leaving food out of a fridge for long periods
   - food going out of date
   - not cooking food for long enough
   - not reheating food thoroughly.

2. Learners should identify that it is better for service users' self-esteem and psychological state.

3. Learners should show understanding of the importance of maintaining dignity and independence as much as possible.

2.4 Understand the role, responsibilities and boundaries of personnel in relation to nutrition and well-being

Activity 20

Learners should think about disabilities such as arthritis that would make it difficult for service users to lift a kettle, especially when full, and stroke, which may mean that service users have only one useful hand. This would mean that bowls might slip, so a non-slip mat would resolve this problem.

Question check

1. Learners should identify that the person would need help from a dietician; an occupational therapist and physiotherapist would also be involved. They might suggest a social care worker, and a doctor.

2. The manager's role includes:
   - staff training
   - assessment procedure and documentation
   - referrals
   - resources
   - quality of food
   - medication.

3. Diet and well-being

3.1 Understand what constitutes a well balanced diet

You could discuss with learners the wealth of advice that is published about what we should and should not be eating, and how confusing this is. The National Nutritional Guidelines are a simple guide to follow and more emphasis should be placed on learners really understanding those and putting this advice into practice in their work role in an appropriate way.

Activity 21

Learners can use this self-assessment to reflect on their own practice.

Activity 22

This activity introduces learners to judging how healthy food is from the labelling of ingredients. It should be emphasised that hidden ingredients may make foods more unhealthy than they had realised.

Activity 23

Learners could use deduction from the information given on food packages to answer this task.

Activity 24

This is another activity intended to enable learners to increase their skills and confidence in using the Internet. The leaflets may be available at your local NHS resource centre. There is also a DVD which can be shown to the learners.

Question check

1. Heart disease, stroke, breast cancer.
2. More starch and fibre, less sugar.
3. A mineral that is only required in tiny amounts, but is essential to health.
4. Improves night vision, keeps lining of mucous membranes healthy, is an anti-oxidant.

3.2 Understand the factors to consider when purchasing food and drink

This section guides the learners through making choices about the food by looking at the pros and cons of buying fresh foods compared to commercially produced alternatives. Learners need to appreciate that it is not as simple as assuming fresh is always best, as sometimes there is a balance to be struck between convenience, the capabilities of the service user, cooking and storage facilities available and access to shops or a shopper.

Activity 25

This activity is designed to encourage learners to try some 'back to basics' cookery. It can also be used to stimulate debate about whether commercially produced foods are less nutritious or less tasty than home-processed ones.

Activity 26

Learners should show their understanding of cooking methods that retain nutrients without adding fat.

Activity 27

Learners should identify that Bran Flakes are better for anaemia and obesity and Fruit and Fibre would be a better choice for service users with high blood pressure and constipation.

Activity 28

This activity should increase learners' confidence and skills in interpreting the information on food labels.

Activity 29

In this realistic activity, learners need to be able to compare similar products to ensure that service users' limited budgets stretch as far as possible.

Question check

1. Because the vitamin levels fall as vegetables age.
2. No difference, unless fresh vegetables have been allowed to deteriorate.
3. High sugar or high salt content.
4. Fruit is now available in fruit juice as well as syrup; low-salt versions of canned vegetables can be found for some product lines.
5. Vitamins pass into the water so are lost, unless used to make the gravy.

3.3 Understand the importance of appropriate storage of food and drink

This section gives basic advice about safe storage of foods. The aim is to reinforce good practice and is particularly important for community care assistants, who may need to advise service users, or check on frail individuals to ensure they are not being put at unnecessary risk.

Question check

1. 4°C to ensure it does not exceed 8°C.

2. At the bottom of the fridge to ensure blood does not drip on ready-to-eat foods.

3. They are still edible, but would probably not taste as good as they should.

4. Use a cool box with ice blocks in it. Put frozen food away in the freezer as soon as possible.

5. Transfer to a non-metallic container, cover and store in the fridge. Eat within 2 days.

3.4 Understand the importance of using the most appropriate method of cooking and reheating food

Learners should be fully aware of the healthiest ways to cook foods, and safe ways to keep food hot. Those working in the community should look out for service users risking food poisoning when saving meals for later, for example if meals-on-wheels arrive too early, or the service user is not hungry at the time.

Reflection, page 110

This is another opportunity for care workers to try new techniques at home when preparing their own meals, thus increasing skills and confidence.

Question check

1. Steaming, stir-frying with olive oil, and poaching.

2. Olive oil is the healthiest, but sunflower oil and other vegetable oils are less harmful than animal fats.

3. Food must be thoroughly heated through, with no cool spots. It must be piping hot.

4. 63°C.

4. Legislation relevant to providing food and drink

4.1 Understand the legislation, regulations and guidance that govern nutrition and food preparation and handling

This section guides learners through the legislation they need to understand and follow when dealing with preparation and provision of food and drink in a care setting. Most learners find legislation tedious, so activities have been included to relate law to practice as much as possible.

As a tutor you should check for new legislation before delivering this section and always teach about the law at the current time.

Activity 30

Example answers:

Employer's responsibilities	
Carry out risk assessments	Complete a risk assessment for service users cooking for themselves
Ensure policies and procedures are in place	Food hygiene policy
Provide safety equipment	Oven gloves
Record all accidents and incidents	Cuts, burns & scalds, food poisoning
Ensure workplace is fully insured	Employer's Compulsory Liability Insurance and Public Liability Insurance must be up to date
Ensure staff are properly trained	Staff have completed food hygiene certificate
Employee's responsibilities	
Use equipment provided properly	Take care with sharp knives
Report hazards	Cracked work surface should be reported to manager
Take care of own and other people's health and safety	Do not serve food you are at all unsure about
Attend health and safety training	Learn how to use slicing machine properly
Follow policies and procedures	Check dates on food every day

Activity 31

a = 6   f = 4

b = 2   g = 8

c = 9   h = 5

d = 7   i = 1

e = 3

Activity 32

This activity is intended to encourage learners to compare the practice at their place of work against best practice. It may also help them to understand the importance of following procedures, and acknowledge that these are there for a reason.

Do take time to discuss with learners the National Minimum Standards and reinforce the ethos of putting the service user at the centre of practice and to empathise with service users.

A video is available for loan from the RCN library that is worth showing to learners if you are able to. It features different service users, including those with confusion, and highlights the difficulties associated with assessing the nutritional state of service users.

Question check

1. Food Safety Act 1990 and Food Safety (General Food Hygiene) Regulations 1985.

2. Under the Human Rights Act.

3. If it was felt their life was in danger.

4. Service users should receive a varied, appealing, wholesome and nutritious diet, suited to individual assessed and recorded requirements. Meals should be taken in a pleasant setting at flexible times.

··

4.2 Understand the organisation's policies and procedures with regard to nutrition and well-being, food and drink preparation and presentation

··

As all organisations' policies and procedures are individual, the tutor could ask learners to bring in policies to compare similarities and differences and discuss the reasons for this.

Activity 33

This activity raises an opportunity to emphasise the importance of following all the advice in the course, and the danger of cutting corners when no one is watching you.

Student log

The following tables have been reproduced with the kind permission of Skills for Care. Use these tables to log your progress during your training and record the learning outcomes you have covered. The tables may also be used to map the content of an NVQ qualification or other relevant training course. For full details of how the knowledge set for nutrition and well-being cross-references NVQ units, Common Induction Standards and GSCC Code of Practice (workers), please see the Skills for Care knowledge set document at www.skillsforcare.org.uk.

Main area	Learning outcome	Learning outcome achieved (manager's or trainer's signature)	Date
1. Preparation/ presentation of food and drink	1.1 Understand the common factors which affect dietary requirements: ■ Age ■ Culture (also special events/ occasions) ■ Religion/faith tradition ■ Medical conditions and allergies (dysphagia, diabetes, coeliac disease, renal disease, mental health, physical disability, etc.) ■ Personal choice (vegetarian/ vegan; menu; photographs of food and drink) ■ Timing and availability of food and drink		
	1.2 Understand the importance of the appropriate preparation and presentation of food and drink: ■ Food hygiene ■ Personal hygiene (worker and individual) ■ Consistency and texture of food and drink ■ Temperature of food and drink ■ Variety ■ Attractive appearance of food and drink (colour, layout) ■ Portion size		

Main area	Learning outcome	Learning outcome achieved (manager's or trainer's signature)	Date
	■ Supplementary/ complementary foods ('PEG' feeds – see Glossary) ■ Reconstitution and moulding of food ■ Individuals are enabled to prepare their own food as appropriate		
	1.3 Understand the importance of creating an appropriate environment in which to eat and drink, including (where relevant to the working environment): ■ Choice of eating area and companions (dining room, bedroom, lounge, outdoors) ■ Positioning and support of individual to aid swallowing, digestion and general comfort ■ An attractive and clean environment (correctly laid table/tray, cutlery, crockery, cruet, table coverings/mats, napkins/other protection for clothing) ■ Aids to facilitate eating and drinking (special crockery and cutlery, plate guard, cup with spout, dentures, spectacles, hearing aids) ■ In residential setting – restaurant-style layout and serve one table at a time ■ Position of worker if assisting an individual with eating and drinking ■ Ensure individuals are not rushed through their meals		

Main area	Learning outcome	Learning outcome achieved (manager's or trainer's signature)	Date
2. Roles and boundaries	2.1 Understand the role, responsibilities and boundaries of the worker with regard to following the policies and procedures of the care setting on assessment of dietary requirements: ■ Person-centred approach ■ Nutritional screening (recognising malnutrition) ■ Care planning ■ Risk assessment ■ Oral health		
	2.2 Understand the role, responsibilities and boundaries of the worker in relation to monitoring the condition and therapies of the individual: ■ Documentation and record-keeping ■ Observing and reporting concerns ■ Seeking advice and guidance ■ Education of individuals and their significant others		
	2.3 Understand the role, responsibilities and boundaries of the worker in relation to handling and serving food: ■ Personal hygiene ■ Food hygiene ■ Promoting independence ■ Assisted feeding		

Main area	Learning outcome	Learning outcome achieved (manager's or trainer's signature)	Date
	2.4 Understand the roles, responsibilities and boundaries of personnel in relation to nutrition and well-being: ■ Social care worker ■ Workers not involved in direct care (cook, administrator, ancillary worker) ■ Managers (registered, senior) ■ Specialist personnel (medical personnel, dietician, speech and language therapist, occupational therapist, physiotherapist)		
3. Diet and wellbeing	3.1 Understand what constitutes a well-balanced diet: ■ Water ■ Carbohydrates ■ Proteins ■ Fats ■ Minerals ■ Vitamins ■ Fibre		
	3.2 Understand the factors to consider when purchasing food and drink: ■ Fresh food (availability) ■ Frozen foods ■ Processed food (canned, ready meals) ■ Nutritional values ■ Cost and value for money ■ Supporting individuals to work within budgets		

Main area	Learning outcome	Learning outcome achieved (manager's or trainer's signature)	Date
	3.3 Understand the importance of appropriate storage of food and drink, including carriage and delivery, and incorporating stock rotation: ■ Refrigerator (temperature, hygiene) ■ Freezer (temperature, star-rated [*] compartments) ■ Dry cupboard ■ Larder		
	3.4 Understand the importance of using the most appropriate method of cooking and reheating food (steaming, roasting, baking, microwaving, frying) according to: ■ Care setting (community, residential) ■ The needs of the individual		
4. Legislation and guidance related to food and drink	4.1 Understand the legislation, regulations and guidance that govern nutrition and food preparation and handling: ■ Health and Safety at Work Act 1974 ■ Management of Health and Safety at Work Act (amended 1994) ■ Food Safety Act 1990 ■ The food safety (General Food Hygiene) regulations (Department of Health 1995) ■ Human Rights Act 1998 ■ Care Standards Act 2000 ■ Health Act 1999 ■ Community Care Act 1990 ■ Mental Health Act 1983 ■ Data Protection Act 1998		

Main area	Learning outcome	Learning outcome achieved (manager's or trainer's signature)	Date
	■ Disability Discrimination Act 1995 and updates ■ National Service Framework for Older People ■ RCN guidelines – Clinical Study 17 'Recipe for change'		
	4.2 Understand the organisation's policies and procedures with regard to nutrition and well-being, food and drink preparation and presentation		

Glossary

allergen   a substance that can cause an allergic reaction in sensitive people when the immune system recognises them as foreign. They cause no response at all in most people

amino acids   the building blocks of proteins

anorexia nervosa   an eating disorder which is a serious illness, with a death rate of between 10% and 20%. The most frequent causes of death are starvation, dehydration, imbalance of electrolytes (essential minerals in the blood), infections, heart failure and suicide

antioxidants   substances thought to lower the risk of developing cancer and heart disease. They also reduce the chance of oils, fats and fat-soluble vitamins combining with oxygen and causing damage in the body, changing colour, or going rancid

body mass index (BMI)   weight (in kilograms) divided by height (in metres squared), used as a measure of nutritional status

calorific value   the number of calories a food contains

carbohydrate (starches and sugars)   a source of energy in foods such as pasta, rice, bread, potatoes

care plan   a plan that sets out in detail the way daily care and support must be provided for an individual. This plan must be documented, and may also be known as an 'individual plan', ' plan of support', etc.

care planning   the process of producing a care plan using a team approach and including the individual, their family and friends

centile   a method of comparing a child's weight and height to others of the same age, e.g. 0.4th centile – 99.6% of children of the same age will be heavier/taller than a child on this centile

cleft palate   a condition where the roof of the mouth is not fully formed, meaning there is a hole joining the mouth and nose

cognitive behavioural therapy   a therapy that helps people to replace negative thoughts and actions with positive ones

complementary food   nutritional products providing all the nutrients usually present in a well-balanced meal

consistency   the degree of viscosity or firmness of a food

constipation   difficulty in opening the bowels

contamination   the spread of germs from one food or object to another

dehydration   a reduction of 1% or more of the body's normal water content. Depending on the percentage of body weight lost, dehydration can be described as mild, moderate or severe

dependency   relying on something that is addictive, such as illegal drugs or alcohol

dysphagia   difficulty in swallowing

electrolyte balance   the balance of chemicals in the body

fats   sources of energy in foods such as oil, butter, margarine

fibre   a substance in foods such as vegetables and grains that helps towards a healthy working gut

food intolerance   a reaction to particular foods which does not involve an immune response. These can make you feel ill, but are not usually harmful in the same way that a true food allergy might be

Food Standards Agency guidelines   these give us 8 tips for eating well to keep healthy

fructose   a simple sugar found in honey and many ripe fruits

halal   meat from an animal killed in accordance with Muslim ritual whereby it is bled to death

incontinence   passing urine when you don't mean to, due to partial or total loss of control of the bladder

individual   person receiving care and support

laxative   a medicine or tablet that causes a person to open their bowels

Makaton   a system of both hand signs and symbols used by people with learning disabilities who have difficulty using spoken language

malnourished   a person is malnourished when they have not been receiving appropriate nourishment, for example when they have been eating too much or too little of essential nutrients

malnutrition   a state, or condition, where someone is not receiving adequate nourishment. May involve eating too little or too much of essential nutrients

minerals   e.g. calcium, iron, sodium, zinc – essential for maintenance of a healthy body

neural tube defects   spina bifida and hydrocephalus (excess fluid on the brain), conditions that may occur during the development of an unborn baby

nutrition a process that involves the intake, digestion and absorption of nutrient materials (food and drink)

nutritional assessment a detailed review of a patient to establish their nutritional status more accurately

nutritional screening a simple and rapid process of identifying risk factors known to be linked to malnutrition

nutritional screening tool an aid to identify service users at risk of malnutrition

nutritionally balanced diet a diet that includes all the essential elements to prevent malnutrition

overnutrition a condition that results from eating too much food, and often leads to obesity

osteoporosis a condition where the bones, particularly those of the spine, wrists and hips, become thin and weak, and break easily. Often there are no warning signs before a break occurs

PEG (percutaneous endoscopic gastronomy) a feeding tube that passes through the abdominal wall directly into the stomach, so that nutrition can be provided without swallowing, or in some cases to supplement ordinary food (see www.corecharity.org.uk (Digestive Disorders Foundation) factsheet 13)

person-centred approach an approach to care planning and support that empowers individuals to make decisions about what they want to happen in their lives. The decision then provides the basis of any plans that are developed and implemented

phobia an intense fear of something that is harmless

phosphorus if phosphorus builds up in the body it can cause calcium to be lost from the bones, increasing the risk of fractures

protein a nutrient that is needed for growth, repair and maintenance of body, found in foods such as meat, fish, eggs, cheese, milk

psychotherapy a talking therapy used with people with mental ill-health

Patient and Public Involvement (PPI) Forums groups made up of local volunteers who are enthusiastic about influencing and improving the way local health care is delivered

ready-to-eat food that is cooked or raw and will not be cooked again before eating

refer a recommendation for further assessment to another member of health-care team

significant others   the family, friends and advocates of an individual receiving care and support

spina bifida   a condition where the backbone is not properly formed, so that the nerves in the spine may be unprotected, and can cause problems with bladder, bowels and mobility. In more severe cases there is loss of feeling from the waist down

stunted growth   in children, restricted growth

supplementary food   an additional food or drink product that is given to make up for a deficiency identified during a nutritional assessment

texture   the feeling of food in the mouth

undernutrition   a condition that results from eating too little of one or more essential nutrients

unpalatable   not pleasing to the taste

use-by date   the date by which pre-packed food should be used. Food eaten after this date could cause food poisoning

vegetarian   someone who eats no meat or fish or (often) any animal product. There are sub-categories of vegetarianism, depending upon what is excluded from the diet

vermin   pests such as rats, mice, flies and cockroaches, which carry germs that could cause food poisoning

vitamins   a group of substances that are essential in small quantities for normal body function and health, e.g. A,B,C,D,E

wasted   a person is wasted when they have lost muscle

water   a substance essential to life – it prevents dehydration, regulates body temperature, helps prevent strain on kidneys

Bibliography

Bryan, F., Allen, T., Russell, L. (2000) 'The move from a long-stay learning disabilities hospital to community homes; a comparison of clients' nutritional status.' *Journal of Human Nutrition and Dietetics* 13 (4) August 2000 pp 265–270.

Calverley, D., (2007) 'The food fighters,' *Nursing Standard* vol. 21 no. 52 September 2007.

Department of Health (2003), *Care Homes for Older People, National Minimum Standards, Care Homes Regulations*, 2nd ed. The Stationery Office.

Food Standards Agency (2005) *Safer Foods, Better Business*.

Harbottle, L. (2007) *Healthy eating and depression*, Mental Health Foundation.

Kanis, J. A., Melton, L. J., Christiansen, C., Johnston, C. C., Khaltaev, N. 'The diagnosis of osteoporosis.' *J Bone Min Res* 1994; 9:1137–41.

Marshall J., (2004) BBC Fat Nation, *The Big Challenge*, Dorling Kindersley.

Royal College of Nursing (2007) 'Drink to good health.' *Nursing Standard* 22(2) Sept 2007 pp 17–21.

Ruston, D., Hoare, J., Henderson, L., *et al* (2004) *The National Diet and Nutrition Survey: adults aged 19–64 years*. Volume 4: 'Nutritional status (anthropometry and blood analyses), blood pressure and physical activity.' The Stationery Office.

Valios, N., (2007) 'Mean cuisine?' *Community Care* Issue 1672 10 May 2007, pp 34–36.

Websites

www.ageconcern.org.uk

www.bapen.org.uk

www.food.gov.uk

www.eatwell.gov.uk

www.direct.gov.uk

www.rcn.org.uk

Weblinks

The websites and weblinks used in this book were correct and up to date at the time of publication. It is essential for tutors to preview each website before using it so as to ensure that the URL is still accurate, relevant and appropriate.

Page 9

http://www.ageconcern.org.uk/AgeConcern/Documents/Hungry_
to_be_Heard_August_2006.pdf

Page 10

http://www.rcn.org.uk/campaigns/nutritionnow

Page 19

http://dementia.ion.ucl.ac.uk/DRG_Website/Candid/Candid_
factsheets/facts6.htm

Page 20

http://www.dietetics.co.uk/article-nutrition-in-dysphagia.asp

Page 27

http://www.nacc.org.uk/downloads/factsheets/GeneralNurses.pdf

Page 32

http://www.alzheimers.org.uk/site/scripts/documents_info.
php?documentID=365

Page 55

http://www.bapen.org.uk/pdfs/intouch/intouch_43.pdf

http://www.ageconcern.org.uk/AgeConcern/Documents/Hungry_
to_be_Heard_August_2006.pdf

http://www.fhf.org.uk/meetings/2007-03-20_wait.pdf

Page 56

http://www.bapen.org.uk/pdfs/must/must_exec_sum.pdf

Page 62

http://www.rcn.org.uk/campaigns/nutritionnow

Page 94

http://www.eatwell.gov.uk/healthydiet/nutritionessentials/
vitaminsandminerals/#elem226170

Page 110

http://home.howstuffworks.com/low-fat-baking3.htm

Page 112

http://www.direct.gov.uk/en/RightsAndResponsibilities/
Citizensandgovernment/DG_4002951

Index

Illustrations are indicated by **bold** page numbers, tables by *italic*.